THE SCHOLARSHIP SERIES IN BIOLOGY

General Editor : Alan Dale

HEATHLAND ECOLOGY

HEATHLAND ECOLOGY

By
C. P. FRIEDLANDER
B.Sc., A.R.C.S., F.R.E.S.

HARVARD UNIVERSITY PRESS
CAMBRIDGE   MASSACHUSETTS
1961

Printed in Great Britain

TO MY MOTHER

CONTENTS

FIGURES

PLATES

TABLES

PREFACE

THIS book aims at presenting some principles of ecology in general as they are revealed by a study of heathland in particular.

The value of elementary ecology as a discipline, apart from its purely observational and descriptive side, lies largely in the fact that the ecologist is forced to link effects with causes. It is rarely possible to make definite statements about the causes of ecological phenomena without supporting them by experimental evidence obtained either from the field or from the laboratory ; the observer then becomes a scientist. Perhaps the most important principle to be grasped is that plants and animals are interdependent and that both depend on, and contribute to, the soil—a concept which affords opportunity for much experimental work in the correlation of factors. Ecology is thus a meeting-place for many branches of science—mathematics, physics, chemistry and geology—and, provided that these are not allowed to obscure the main issue which must always be the occurrence and behaviour of the organisms, such diversity adds interest to the study and is valuable in demonstrating the essential unity of science as revealed in scientific method which, understandably, is not always apparent to beginners.

No work of this kind is original ; an author cannot recall where he first learned facts and principles, or to whom he owes ways of presenting certain ideas. This book is no exception, and many of those who have contributed to it must remain unacknowledged. Students of ecology cannot overlook the debt to the foundations laid by Sir Arthur Tansley and Dr. Charles Elton, and I am particularly grateful for the enthusiasm which was brought to the subject by those who taught me as an undergraduate at Imperial College. Scarcely less must I thank many of my pupils for so much willingness and patient observation, often in bad weather. They have, often deliberately, contributed to the choice of subject matter used here, to the manner of its presentation and, of course, to the data. To L. Hugh Newman's Natural History Photographic Agency I am indebted for Plates III to VIII. I am grateful to Mr. A. Eve, B.Sc., for information on certain points and to my publisher and the editor of this series for their encouragement and for the great care which has been bestowed on the production of the book from the very beginning.

1960   C. P. F.

CHAPTER I

INTRODUCTION TO HEATHLAND

HEATHLAND offers a good habitat for studying the elements of ecology because of its simplicity as compared with other easily accessible habitats. The paucity of species which is often, rightly, described as a characteristic of heaths is an advantage rather than a drawback for the beginner, by comparison with the richer fauna and flora of woods and water in which no two specimens collected seem alike. Physical factors are immediately apparent on heathland, and their measurement presents little difficulty; furthermore, the relationship of the plant and animal life is easy to see, and local differences in soil conditions often lead directly to an altered flora and fauna, so demonstrating their dependence on environmental factors.

The heathland described in this book is that which is typical of sandy soils in England, namely, soils having a layer of raw humus or 'mor' rarely exceeding 6 inches in depth lying upon the surface of the soil proper. The remarks made here apply to the heaths of Southern England, but most of them apply with equal force to all areas dominated typically by ling or bell heather irrespective of the mode of origin of their soils. Wet heaths are also described.

The change in physical factors may be tested by merely standing on an open heath during a windy and cloudy day. The temperature may drop suddenly as the sun becomes overcast, and under such conditions the chilling effect of the wind is immediately noticed. Conversely, on the same heath a still sunny day may produce conditions of insolation hard to bear. This is a demonstration of extreme conditions of temperature and wind, two factors largely responsible for determining the flora of a habitat and, consequently, its fauna. Fig. 1 illustrates the different temperatures on an open heath and in adjoining woodland, while Table I shows some maximum and minimum temperatures in the two habitats on the same days, at a height of 3 feet above the ground. Brief study of these figures shows that the plants which are to flourish under heathland conditions must exhibit specializations not required by the mesophytes growing in woodland. Given a certain rainfall in the locality, it is clear that evaporation will be greater near ground level on the heath than in the woodland, and heathland plants must therefore overcome

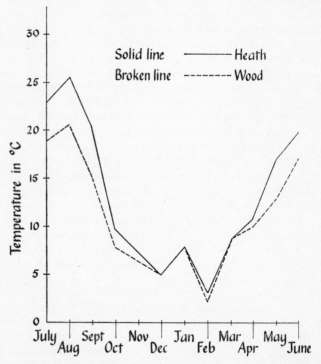

FIG. 1. Graph of noonday air temperature on heath and in adjoining woodland. The temperature for each month was averaged from readings taken weekly at about noon, measured 3 feet above ground level. The difference between heath and woodland temperature is greater in the summer because of insolation.

excessive loss of water and will show the xeromorphic features associated with this need. Also, the mechanical effect of the wind, unbroken by the trunks of woody perennials, reduces the weak herbaceous plants to small proportions, and they are able to grow within the shelter afforded by the dwarf shrubs.

TABLE I

Comparison of extreme air temperatures on heath and in adjoining woodland—degrees Centigrade

DATE	WOOD		HEATH	
	Min.	*Max.*	*Min.*	*Max.*
February 14th–15th	1·5	4	0·5	5
Range . . .	2·5		4·5	
May 2nd–3rd . .	5	13·3	3·6	14·5
Range . . .	8·3		10·9	
June 25th–26th .	14	24	12·5	27
Range . . .	10		14·5	

A further reason for water shortage lies in the mechanical composition of the soil. Fig 2 shows the texture of heathland topsoil as revealed by microscopic examination. Sandy soils consist essentially of particles of silica (SiO_2) which may be either rounded or sharp-edged. In each case they do not pack very tightly and large air spaces remain between them, which have the effect of reducing the soil's capillarity and increasing its porosity. Consequently gravitational water tends to pass through the soil rapidly and soon ceases to be available for absorption by the roots of plants. This water loss is less where the proportion of humus mixed with the sand is high, but unless an impermeable layer lies close under the surface rainfall is effective for only a short time. This may be verified by feeling heathland topsoil with the fingers a few hours after a summer shower. In assessing a soil's field capacity this gravitational water is excluded (see Fig. 3). Most of the water which is available to plants and generally used by them is held by capillary attraction between the soil particles, and when this fraction is consumed the plants tend to wilt. A little more

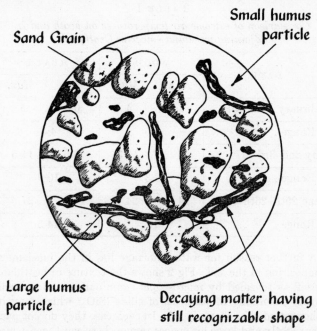

Fig. 2. Part of a slide of the A_1 horizon of a podsol from Pirbright, Surrey. (Mounted in glycerine.)

water can, however, be extracted by the roots; this is the imbibitional water which is held by soil colloids between their molecules as in a gelatine or agar agar gel. If one tries to obtain air-dried soil by spreading it out in a thin layer on blotting paper until its weight is constant, it will be found very difficult to bring it to exactly constant weight; this is due to the imbibition of atmospheric moisture by the dry soil on damp days. Careful air-drying will remove all the water which is obtainable by the plants' roots. A clay soil, however, will still retain a considerable amount of hygroscopic water, that is to say water which actually forms a part of the soil colloids and also which

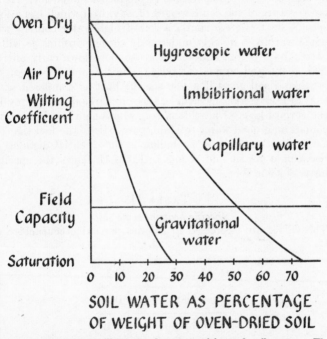

FIG. 3. Diagram to illustrate the composition of soil water. The curve on the left is for sandy soil, that on the right for clay soil. (Slightly altered from W. O. JAMES. *An Introduction to Plant Physiology.* Oxford University Press.)

is held on the surface of the colloidal particles in the form of unimolecular films. The small size and consequent large area of colloidal particles allows much water to be held in this way, and plants can wilt in a clay soil which has a higher gross

water content than a more sandy soil whose water is available
to the plants since it is less strongly held.

Another effect of the soil's mechanical composition is upon
its specific heat; sandy soils are 'warm'. Water has a high
specific heat, that is to say much more heat is required to raise
its temperature than is needed to produce a similar increase in
temperature of the same weight of, say, iron which has a low
specific heat. Consequently a soil of high water content will
not warm up so quickly under early spring sunshine as will a
better drained soil, and this tends to slow down early micro-
bial, plant and animal activity. The low water content of
heathland soil gives it a low specific heat as compared with
that of a clay soil. Of course, these remarks do not apply to
the surface layer of heathland soil, whose high humus content
confers on it good water-retaining properties; the fact that on
a true heath this layer is shallow is the essential distinction
between a heath and a moor. Table II shows the specific
heats of some soils.

TABLE II

Specific heats of some soils

The values are expressed in calories per cubic centimetre of
soil.

Dried sand .	0·3
Dried clay .	0·24
Dried humus .	0·15
Saturated sand .	0·7
Saturated clay .	0·8
Saturated humus	0·9

Adapted from G . W . ROBINSON. *Soils.* Allen & Unwin.

PLATE I

A typical heath on Wimbledon Common. The central mass of ling is competing against invading grasses, chiefly wavy hair-grass, and birch. The effect of trampling upon ling is shown by its disappearance from the sides of the small path on the right.

PLATE II

A Surrey heath in a late stage of colonization. The ling is almost replaced by bracken whose dead fronds occupy the foreground, fairly large birch saplings and some gorse. Scots pine is in the background. This area has passed through the 'birch-pine heath' stage and is becoming woodland.

It is characteristic of heathland that its soil is acidic: it lacks basic ions and on testing with indicators shows a pH of less than seven. The commonest basic ion in soil is calcium, and in general a base-unsaturated soil may be defined as one which is deficient in calcium, that is to say it possesses no free calcium ions for they have already been appropriated by acid radicles. Plants confined to acid soils are known as calcifuges, but apart from the comparatively few strict calcifuges there are several plants which thrive on acidic soils—as well as many others which show a wide range of tolerance of soil reaction. It is therefore evident that soil acidity is a factor which ultimately affects the animal ecology of a habitat. On some Cornish heaths calcifuge species grow side by side with calcicoles which do not tolerate acid soils (Book List, Ref. 4). This anomaly may be due to the fact that the soil is not formed from sand, but is of a clayey nature having a high pH. Although other bases are present there is little available calcium, which permits the growth of calcifuge species, while the presence of bases provides the high pH which enables calcicoles to flourish.

The frequent burning of heaths is a semi-natural feature in this country. It is due to their insolation, but is probably not often caused by the direct solar heat alone. In all parts of the country there are pieces of glass left behind by 'campers' which act as burning glasses, and also heathland is by its nature easily set ablaze by careless firelighting or smoking. The burning, natural or otherwise, is now a regular feature of heaths and helps to perpetuate the habitat by destroying the young trees which might otherwise become established on them. Indirectly it is of use to the ecologist by producing demonstrations of natural regeneration.

CHAPTER II

THE FORMATION OF HEATHLAND

IT is possible to make a good estimate of the distribution of heathland by examining a geological map.* In general, where the 'drift' or surface geology indicates sandstone beds or alluvial gravels heathland may develop. This is not the original vegetation in most cases, neither is it the climatic climax (for reasons discussed in the next chapter) but it is wholly characteristic.

Heathland in Southern England is a degenerate condition caused by the felling of the original temperate forest which was the climatic climax. In Pre-Roman times Southern Britain was thickly covered with forest—oak, ash and beech. The pedunculate oak *Quercus robur* predominated on the heavier clay soils, the sessile oak *Q. petraea* and the ash *Fraxinus excelsior* on the limestone soils in the North and West, and the beech *Fagus sylvatica* on chalk and on the lighter soils in the South. These deductions are made by observing the present distributions of the remaining natural forest. The felling which began seriously with the Romans' clearings around their encampments continued with the growth of towns and the demands of shipbuilding and iron smelting. In many places the felling gave rise to scrub vegetation of various types depending on the nature of the soil—a process which may be observed after felling at the present day —and eventually, unless prevented, this reverted to the climatic climax. The climax did not occur everywhere, and on those sandy soils which may have been primitively rather lacking in basic ions the heathland vegetation developed. The

* Geological maps are issued in two forms: 'solid' showing the underlying rocks, and 'drift' showing surface deposits. It is the drift map which the ecologist uses since the surface layer, even if thin, yields the soil in which the plants' roots grow.

process was assisted by the absence of replanting after the felling, so that fast-growing plants capable of flourishing on slightly acidic soils became established.

Under conditions of high rainfall—the entire British Isles come within this category—the surface of the soil tends to lose its soluble mineral content, which is carried away by the rain water, either directly in solution or as a result of the action of dilute acids in the water. This process is called leaching, and has the effect of lowering the base content of the topsoil and also strips some of the humus content, solid humus particles being carried down mechanically. Clearly leaching will occur much more readily where percolation is rapid than where it is slow, and consequently sandy soils become leached more readily than the heavier clay soils. Even on sandy soils the process is greatly impeded if there is a close-growing cover of vegetation on the surface of the ground, and particularly by the presence of large trees which create a strong upward transpiration stream of water and whose leaves, on falling, decay in situ, thereby returning solutes to the top-soil.

If the leaching continues for a long time, over a few hundred years, a characteristic type of soil is produced, the podsol. Podsols may be recognized in situ by digging a small trench or cutting away at a sloping surface so that a vertical surface about three feet high is exposed. This surface will be seen to consist of several layers, or horizons, which are of different colours and textures, produced from an originally more homogeneous soil by the process of podsolization.* The appearance of a soil in vertical section is called its profile; Fig. 4 shows a typical podsol profile.

In soil profiles it is usual to label the horizons which are being leached as A and those in which the leached material is being deposited as B. In Fig. 4 the horizon A represents the 'raw humus', the characteristic surface layer of heathland. The leaf litter and humus layers are not always distinct from each other on open heath—but in a pine wood an F layer of pine

* Horizons in *soil* must not be confused with the strata of sedimentary *rocks*—each of which consists of rock of a different age.

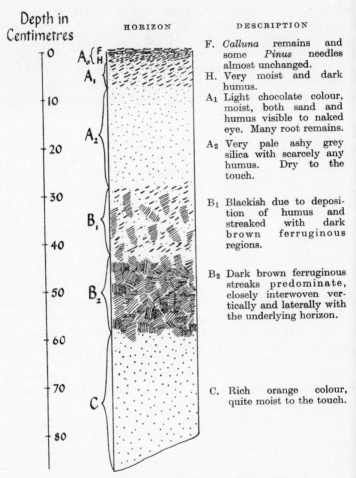

Depth in Centimetres

HORIZON

DESCRIPTION

F. *Calluna* remains and some *Pinus* needles almost unchanged.

H. Very moist and dark humus.

A_1 Light chocolate colour, moist, both sand and humus visible to naked eye. Many root remains.

A_2 Very pale ashy grey silica with scarcely any humus. Dry to the touch.

B_1 Blackish due to deposition of humus and streaked with dark brown ferruginous regions.

B_2 Dark brown ferruginous streaks predominate, closely interwoven vertically and laterally with the underlying horizon.

C. Rich orange colour, quite moist to the touch.

Fig. 4.　Profile of a podsol from Pirbright, Surrey.

needles and twigs is always visible. Horizon C consists of the unchanged underlying material.

An unleached sandy soil contains humus and several salts and other substances depending upon the soil's origin and on the water supply which reaches it. Silica (SiO_2) is not the only mineral in sandy soils: some clay is always present, consisting of hydrated silicates of potassium and aluminium often associated with ferric oxide which imparts a reddish brown colour to the soil. The aluminium in the form of alumina (Al_2O_3), and the iron (Fe_2O_3), may be referred to collectively as the sesquioxides, and they resemble the humus particles in forming part of the colloidal complex of the soil.

Podsols develop if the following conditions are present:—

(i) a low base content,

(ii) good drainage, and

(iii) rainfall sufficient to overcome water lost by evaporation from the soil and from plants.

Under conditions of low base content the typical heath plants, ling and pine for example, are able to colonize felled ground very readily because, for reasons which are not understood, they do not require much calcium and this gives them an advantage over the deciduous forest vegetation whose calcium requirements are greater. The heath plants yield leaf litter, which lacks calcium and is therefore acidic and not readily attacked by bacteria, so that a layer of raw humus accumulates—this is the A_0 and part of the A_1 horizon. The leaf litter imparts organic acids to the water which percolates through it and they cause the clay fraction of the soil to release the sesquioxides, which together with humus are carried down in to the B horizon. Absence of calcium assists this process. If it were present, especially as calcium bicarbonate, which ionizes readily, it would tend to make the colloids flocculate—i.e. form aggregate particles or 'crumbs' which would resist the downward mechanical force of the water.

The A_2 horizon appears as an ashy grey colour because these materials have been removed from it. In the case of a well established podsol on originally siliceous material this horizon may consist of fairly pure silica, which is both chemically and mechanically an unsatisfactory medium for plants' rooting systems. Not only the colloids but also the mineral salts in crystalloid solution have been leached from the A_2 and the infertility of podsols now becomes evident. Of course podsols *can* be restored to fertility by deep ploughing, which brings the colloidal complex from the B horizons to the topsoil once more, and by the addition of lime and phosphates. Such agriculture, however, is costly, and the best large scale use of heathland is as coniferous plantation. The conifers thrive on podsols, and the Forestry Commission is planting conifers on large areas of the Scottish hills which are at present put to very little use.

It is only fair to say that the account of podsol formation given here in very dogmatic terms is vastly oversimplified, and much remains to be discovered—especially about the metabolism of the plants whose low base requirements hasten the process, and about the behaviour of the soil colloids.

In Scotland large areas of 'heather moor' are really heathland. Moor in the strict sense of the word is always wet and has accumulated a layer of peat many feet thick, while the dominant plants are neither *Calluna* nor *Erica* but the sedges *Trichophorum caespitosum* or *Eriophorum* spp. and, under slightly drier conditions, mat-grass, *Nardus stricta*. Such moor can form on soils other than those originally poor in bases, and its origin depends on climatic conditions rather than soil (edaphic) conditions.

Once podsolization has occurred deciduous forest has difficulty in re-establishing itself—with the exception of birch which seems to grow anywhere—on account of the impoverished nature of the soil. In addition to this, because of the grazing action of animals neither birch nor pine grows readily unless enclosed, and consequently heathland tends to perpetuate itself.

Heaths may develop elsewhere than on true podsols if the soil can provide the essential podsol features although it may have been formed in quite a different way. Such is the case with the 'chalk heathlands' which occur in several localities on the South Downs (Book List, Ref. 1). Here, although the underlying rock is chalk the surface vegetation has strong heathland characteristics. This may be due to the deposition of wind-blown material poor in calcium carbonate supporting a flora which masks the true nature of the underlying chalk.

Of course, in practice the dry heath whose formation has been described does not occur uniformly over a wide area. Even in the South streams flowing across heaths will produce local changes of vegetation. The formation of these streams is due to the geography of the area, and as a rule they are shallow and do not contain very much water, since water tends to sink through rather than to flow over the sandy ground. If the underlying strata, however, consist of impervious material the streams may well lead into a central bog and around a central area of free water there may extend a 'wet heath'. This is quite different in origin from the mountain bog which is the result of continuous high rainfall. The fate of the heath will depend on events which occur outside it—generally an area of marshy ground tends to dry out due to the effect of transpiration of the vegetation encroaching upon it, and this tendency will not be reversed unless the amount of water entering the marsh increases. Consequently, in the South bogs are rare, and are to be found only on low ground under suitable soil conditions with a very regular water supply.

SOIL ANALYSIS

Before leaving the subject of soil a few remarks on the method of analysing it may be found useful.

In making a soil analysis as part of elementary fieldwork it is important to keep the analysis simple. If this is not done the soil part of the work may become so involved and time-consuming that one loses sight of the main purpose of the study. As in any experimental work it is of no use to take some of the readings to great accuracy if they are to be correlated with measurements which cannot be so accurately made.

Table III

Result of simple analysis of a Podsol from Pirbright, Surrey

	HORIZON					
	A_1	A_2	B_1	B_2	C	
Loosely held water as a percentage of weight of wet soil	41·5	9·6	16·7	15·7	15·9	
Strongly held water as a percentage of weight of air-dried soil	5·4	0·8	2·1	1·6	1·1	
Humus content as a percentage of weight of air-dried soil	23·5	3·4	33·1	1·9	2·2	
Mineral content as a percentage of weight of air-dried soil	71·1	95·8	64·8	96·5	96·7	
Air space as a percentage of volume of air-dried soil .	61	44	45	42	48	
pH	5·7	7	7	7	6·4	

Generally, counts of organisms can be made only within a wide range of error, and so there is little point in pushing the refinements of the soil analysis too far. These remarks apply to simple field ecology; clearly under the rigorously controlled conditions of agricultural research the position is quite different.

Soil samples

The soil should be taken from a freshly cut profile rather than drawn up with an auger. It should be transferred at once to a thick plastic bag and tightly sealed and labelled with site, horizon, date and a note about the recent weather. This label is best put inside the bag.

Analysis

Soil from each horizon should be analysed for its water, humus, mineral and air ratios—and also for pH and calcium carbonate content. Most of the figures are expressed as percentages of the air-dried soil (A.D.S.), to obtain which it is sufficient to lay out the soil, slightly crushed, on blotting paper until it dries to constant weight. The reason for using A.D.S. as a basis, rather than the wet soil as taken from the ground, is that gravitational water varies with the weather whereas the A.D.S. has constant properties and is therefore a better standard for comparison. (This does not alter the fact that the effective proportions of water and air in the soil vary greatly with rainfall, and in consistently very wet places with almost water-logged soil the true air content bears little resemblance to that which is obtained from a test on A.D.S.) Table III shows the result of a simple soil analysis.

(i) *Water content.* The proportion of loosely held water is determined by the loss in weight on drying a weighed sample of soil in air. This is called the loosely held water since most of it is available to plants, and it is expressed as a percentage of the weight of wet soil taken from the ground. The proportion of strongly held soil water (*i.e.* the hygroscopic water) is expressed as a percentage of the A.D.S. It is determined by gently warming a weighed quantity of A.D.S. in a crucible, stirring all the time. Not much soil should be used for there is a danger of burning the humus; when this happens a characteristic smell is given off by the various breakdown products such as dextrins. After being warmed the soil is allowed to cool, in a desiccator, and then weighed. The process is repeated until two successive weighings tally, and then all the water may be assumed to have been driven off. The desiccator must be used in order to prevent reabsorption of water by the cooling colloids. The warming process is carried out much more accurately, of course, in an oven at 105 degrees Centigrade.

(ii) *Humus content.* This percentage is obtained by heating

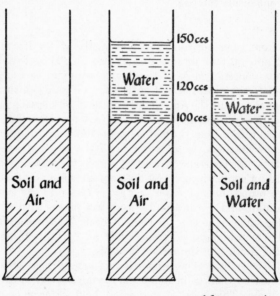

After gentle
tapping of the jar

FIG. 5. Estimation of air space in a soil sample. This sample of air-dried soil contains 30 per cent. by volume of air.

the soil from the previous determination in the crucible in order to burn off the humus, stirring all the time and cooling to constant weight as before. The heating may be done effectively in a muffle furnace. Where soil contains a high proportion of calcium carbonate it too will be decomposed, thus giving a false value to the humus reading, but with heathland soil this may be disregarded.

(iii) *Mineral content.* Estimation of the various elements present is not a simple process, and therefore the mineral percentage is found merely by subtraction of the humus and water from the A.D.S.

(iv) *Air content.* This may be determined by displacement of air when water is poured on to a column of A.D.S. packed, if possible, as tight as it was when in situ. If it is packed into a measuring cylinder the volume of air may be read off directly. The soil sample in Fig. 5, for example, contains 30 per cent. of air space.

(v) *pH.* A simple test will suffice. A few cubic centimetres of the soil are shaken up in ten cubic centimetres of distilled water in a boiling tube and three drops of Universal Indicator added. The contents are given time to settle and the colour of the water is compared with the scale on the bottle label. A very little practice enables one to dispense with the scale. More precise determinations can be obtained by using the separate indicators for the acid range in the same way as above.

Bromo-cresol green: sensitive between pH 3·8 and 5·4
Chlor-phenol red: ,,   ,,   ,, 4·8 and 6·4
Bromo-thymol blue: ,,   ,,   ,, 5·8 and 7·4

There are more accurate ways of finding pH involving apparatus for use in critical work, but the method described here is quite good enough for elementary purposes, provided that the glassware is well washed beforehand with distilled water and that time is allowed for most of the cloudiness to settle. It helps, too, to view the tube against a matt-white surface.

(vi) *Calcium carbonate content.* This is best determined by observing the reaction of well crushed soil to a few drops of dilute hydrochloric acid. The soil may be placed either in a dish and watched for bubbles, or in a boiling tube and held against the ear for the characteristic crackling sound when the carbon dioxide is being evolved. Either way calls for practice and it is a good plan to prepare standards of one's own by taking burnt soil and making it up into samples containing 1 per cent. calcium carbonate, 0·5 per cent. calcium carbonate, and a trace of calcium carbonate, well mixed in. The test sample may then be checked against these standards. The same quantity of acid of the same strength should always be used.

CHAPTER III

THE BOTANY OF HEATHLAND

THERE is no denying that heaths everywhere are very much alike, on account of the uniform edaphic conditions and the characteristic flora. Whether this leads to uninteresting scenery is a matter of opinion—but it is true to say that knowing the geographical position and soil moisture of a given piece of heath one could compose a fairly accurate species list without actually visiting it.

When considering heathland botany we must always keep in mind that we are dealing with an unstable community whose species are kept in check by several factors, and that we must expect to find various degrees of heath depending on the strength of the various factors in the locality at any given time—a dynamic equilibrium in fact. The general relationship of a heath to neighbouring habitats is discussed below and summarized diagrammatically in Fig. 13, p. 36.

The most widespread dominant on dry heath is ling heather, *Calluna vulgaris*, a small evergreen shrub with a shallow rooting system. In Britain it is well within its distribution range, and so flourishes wherever conditions are suitable. Its great significance is that it contributes a distinct layer giving shelter from wind and extremes of temperature and humidity to smaller plants—and animals—beneath it. There are, in fact, layers on heathland corresponding to those in woodland, with the dwarf shrubs taking the place of the trees. Fig. 6 illustrates this layering. *Calluna* though tough and woody does not tolerate excessive trampling, and this is why parts of heath close to paths and human habitation tend to lose their ling and become invaded by tough grasses which are also characteristic of the habitat. The rather slow growth of ling from seed is another factor which assists this process.

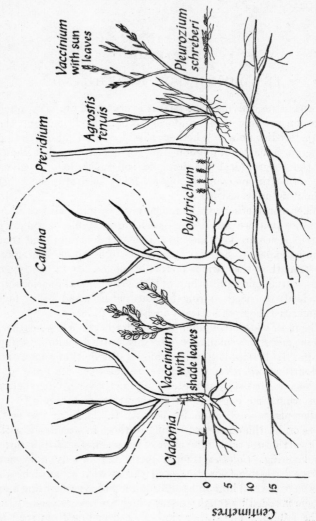

FIG. 6. Layering and vertical distribution of root systems of representative heathland plants.

Sometimes occurring as a dominant, but more often as a subsidiary layer under the ling, is the bilberry or whortleberry, *Vaccinium myrtillus*. Where ling is absent, especially on higher ground, bilberry can become dominant. It is able to thrive on the same ground as ling because it uses a different part of the soil profile, thereby reducing competition. Fig 6 illustrates this vertical distribution of rooting systems. Clearly in a 'poor' soil such a distribution assumes even greater importance than it does elsewhere, and differences in level of an inch or two may serve to separate the main constituents of the flora. The result of a simple soil analysis, showing the composition of the soil at different levels (as described in the previous chapter) is given in Table III.

Vaccinium is a variable plant, bearing 'sun' and 'shade' leaves. Sun leaves are xeromorphic adaptations and are produced when the plant grows in exposed situations, such as after burning on heathland (page 31), while shade leaves are produced under sheltered conditions as in woodland. The shade leaves are larger, paler and less heavily cuticularized—whether they are produced as a reaction to shade itself, or rather to the higher humidity associated with shade conditions, is not quite certain. These points are illustrated in Fig. 10.

The bracken fern, *Pteridium aquilinum*, is dominant on some heaths—being especially abundant near existing or felled woodland. Its stout rhizomes which branch freely lead to rapid colonization, and the deep shade which it casts allows very little to grow beneath it, except for bryophytes in the moister places. Bracken can thus shade out almost all other heathland vegetation, but for reasons which are not clear it generally fails to cover the entire area apparently available. A very careful study of the edaphic features of bracken and non-bracken parts of the same heath suggests itself as a suitable piece of fieldwork. Perhaps soil moisture holds the key to the problem.

Grasses are certainly constituents of heath and it is sometimes difficult to say where heathland ends and grassland proper begins. On suitable acidic soils it is best not to make too fine a distinction on account of the dynamic equilibrium

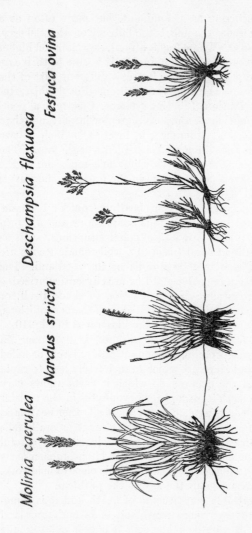

FIG. 7. The mode of growth of some heathland grasses.

PLATE III

Small heath butterfly resting on cross-leaved heath, *Erica tetralix*.

PLATE IV

Common lizard.   This specimen's original tail has been lost and it has grown a fresh one.

already mentioned. *Deschampsia flexuosa*, the wavy hair-grass, is frequently co-dominant with ling. It possesses slender rhizomes and does not usually occupy the whole of the ground but allows other plants to grow with it. Rhizomes are not invariably present, and the grass can grow in loose tufts—but even so it does not monopolise the ground. Some grasses, however, which have the tufted mode of growth do cover the ground to the exclusion of other species—for example the mat-grass, *Nardus stricta*, which is found locally abundant in the South and occupies large areas on hills in Northern England and Scotland. *Nardus* grows so closely packed that it excludes other vegetation. Fig. 7 illustrates the mode of growth.

Trampling is one factor which encourages the spread of grasses at the expense of ling—altitude is another. Ling rarely occurs above two thousand feet, and even below this altitude it grows less vigorously than on low ground. The common bent, *Agrostis tenuis*, and sheep's fescue, *Festuca ovina*, may replace ling on upland heaths, and even in the South they may become dominant as a result of excessive grazing. It is probably true to say that wavy hair-grass is more widespread on lowland heaths than either of these two grasses.

The bell or Scots heather, *Erica cinerea*, may replace ling or may be co-dominant. Both plants may be found growing close together, a slight increase in local humidity favouring the ling. The bell heather produces the same microclimatic conditions as the *Calluna*, providing shelter for similar species of plants and animals, and being equally susceptible to trampling and grazing. *Erica* and *Calluna* are thus ecologically similar. In moist places the cross-leaved heath, *Erica tetralix*, often replaces them.

On ground not covered by ling, or amongst some of the grasses, the sheep's sorrel, *Rumex acetosella*, is very common. Sometimes it grows in such abundance that its reddish-brown inflorescences and fruits impart a characteristic tint to the heath. It is a most variable plant both in size and in leaf shape, leaves on the same plant being very different. Fig. 8 gives an indication of the range of shape and size. Some

Fig. 8. Variation in leaf shape of *Rumex acetosella*.

measurements of the sizes of corresponding leaves, linked with ecological observation, should provide fieldwork for a Natural History group, but the workers may have to be satisfied with negative results. *Rumex acetosella* stands up well to trampling and is most plentiful on the less isolated heaths. In such places, and in exposed situations, it exhibits dwarf forms, while in more humid conditions it is larger and perhaps more variable. However, the solution to the leaf shape problem is unlikely to be a simple matter of humidity.

Two plantains, the buck's-horn plantain, *Plantago coronopus*, and ribwort, *P. lanceolata*, are often found, the former being characteristic. Their rosette habit enables them to succeed in the more exposed places and *P. coronopus* especially stands up well to trampling.

One cannot help being struck by the presence on heaths in all parts of the country of two small species, the heath bed-straw, *Galium hercynicum*, and tormentil, *Potentilla erecta*. They are weak straggling perennials which use the grass or heather to some extent for support. When in blossom the *Galium hercynicum* colours parts of the heath white in spite of the small size of the individual flowers. *G. boreale*, the Northern bedstraw, gradually replaces it in the North and in Scotland.

The gorse, *Ulex europaeus*, is very common on heaths though by no means confined to them, being found also in woods. It certainly prefers soils low in bases. As a member of the heath-land association it may form small communities but more fre-quently grows as isolated bushes. Its seeds are scattered some little distance from the bush by an explosive mechanism, but the reason for their wider distribution is their attractiveness to ants, which drag them by their brightly coloured caruncles and abandon them by the side of small paths across the heath. Dwarf gorse, *Ulex minor*, grows in similar situations but is less common. It is probably often overlooked and thought to be a 'small gorse bush'—but it may be distinguished from *U. europaeus* by its glabrous sepals and lemon-yellow petals, amongst other features.

Another leguminous shrub the broom, *Sarothamnus sco-*

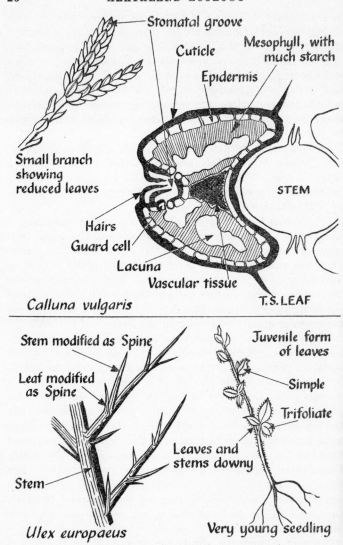

Stomatal groove

Cuticle

Mesophyll, with much starch

Epidermis

Small branch showing reduced leaves

STEM

Hairs

Guard cell

Lacuna

Vascular tissue

Calluna vulgaris

T.S. LEAF

Stem modified as Spine

Leaf modified as Spine

Stem

Ulex europaeus

Juvenile form of leaves

Simple

Trifoliate

Leaves and stems downy

Very young seedling

FIG. 9. Some xeromorphic adaptations.

parius, is more confined to sandy habitats than is the gorse. It is common but generally not abundant even though it is one of the most rabbit-resistant plants.

The *Rhododendron* grows readily on heaths. It is not native but may be locally abundant and even dominant as an escape from cultivation. The main reason for mentioning it here is that it is a member of the Ericaceae, the family to which ling, *Erica,* and *Vaccinium* belong.

Ulex is of course an example of xeromorphic modification, with both stems and leaves forming spines and reducing the area over which transpiration occurs. However this modification is absent from the first few leaves of the seedling, which have the trifoliate form common amongst the Leguminosae and are also softly downy. It can be observed that seedlings growing close to the parent plant show these juvenile features more pronouncedly than do those growing in less sheltered positions. If young seedlings are brought to the laboratory and grown in a moist place, such as an aquarium tank with some standing water and a loosely fitting lid, juvenile features can be maintained until the plant is nine inches high, and perhaps even further. This illustrates the importance of environment in determining form.

The whole question of xeromorphy is a difficult one, and xeromorphic modifications are sometimes seen where they appear to serve no function. The acicular leaves of *Pinus sylvestris* growing, for example, on dry open heaths can be understood in terms of water conservation, but it is less easy to see why the leaves of a similar tree growing in the Highlands should require the adaptation. Similarly the general structure of *Potentilla erecta* shows no apparently significant difference from that of a woodland *Potentilla,* e.g. *P. sterilis,* and yet in this case we might have expected some modification. Probably some features are genetically fixed and others are more readily influenced by habitat factors—e.g. *Vaccinium* and *Ulex* leaves. A useful experiment would be to grow some heathland plants in as moist an environment as they could bear and to compare their morphology, by means of sections and careful external

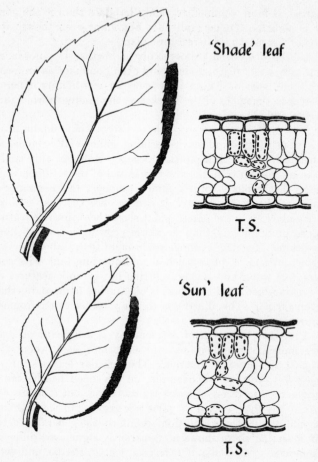

'Shade' leaf

T. S.

'Sun' leaf

T. S.

Vaccinium myrtillus

Sun and shade leaves drawn to same scale.
In each case the leaf drawn was the youngest
but one on the stem.

FIG. 10.   Further examples of xeromorphy.

measurements, with that of plants growing normally.

Xeromorphy may generally be attributed to a water shortage of some kind. Common causes of shortage are:

(*a*) *Physical;* such as porosity of the soil, low rainfall, steep slope of the ground. This is a case of 'not enough water'.

(*b*) *Dryness of the air;* this is really a special case of physical drought. The low humidity raises the rate at which water evaporates from the plants and from the surface of the soil, and this in turn may lead to a shortage of water in the soil.

(*c*) *High temperature and wind;* these factors, although independent of the humidity, increase the drying power of the atmosphere and raise the transpiration rate.

(*d*) *Physiological drought;* the 'coldness' of clay soils making the absorption of water by the roots a difficult process.

On our heaths the cause of water shortage is presumably to be found amongst those in (*a*), (*b*), and (*c*). Although at a first glance the various xeromorphic modifications would seem to be means of reducing water loss, it is by no means true to say that heath plants have a lower rate of transpiration. The function of the thick cuticles is probably to cut down water loss only after a certain threshold has been exceeded, thereby preventing irreparable damage to the protoplasm. The sunken stomata, protective hairs and devices for inrolling of leaves are probably best considered in this light. Figs. 9, 10, and 11 illustrate various examples of xeromorphy.

Grasses flourish in locally moist places. *Holcus lanatus,* Yorkshire fog, is characteristic but by no means confined to acidic soils. It extends on to the drier ground, growing there rather less freely, and may form a junction with its congener *H. mollis* growing near the edges of deciduous woods—a nice instance of ecological distinction between closely related species. The heath grass, *Sieglingia decumbens,* grows best under moist conditions and is very common. Purple moor-grass, *Molinia caerulea,* grows abundantly in very wet places, either where wet heath merges on to open water or else on upland slopes. It is by no means unusual to find it in small quantities on dry heaths, but there it is never a dominant. On

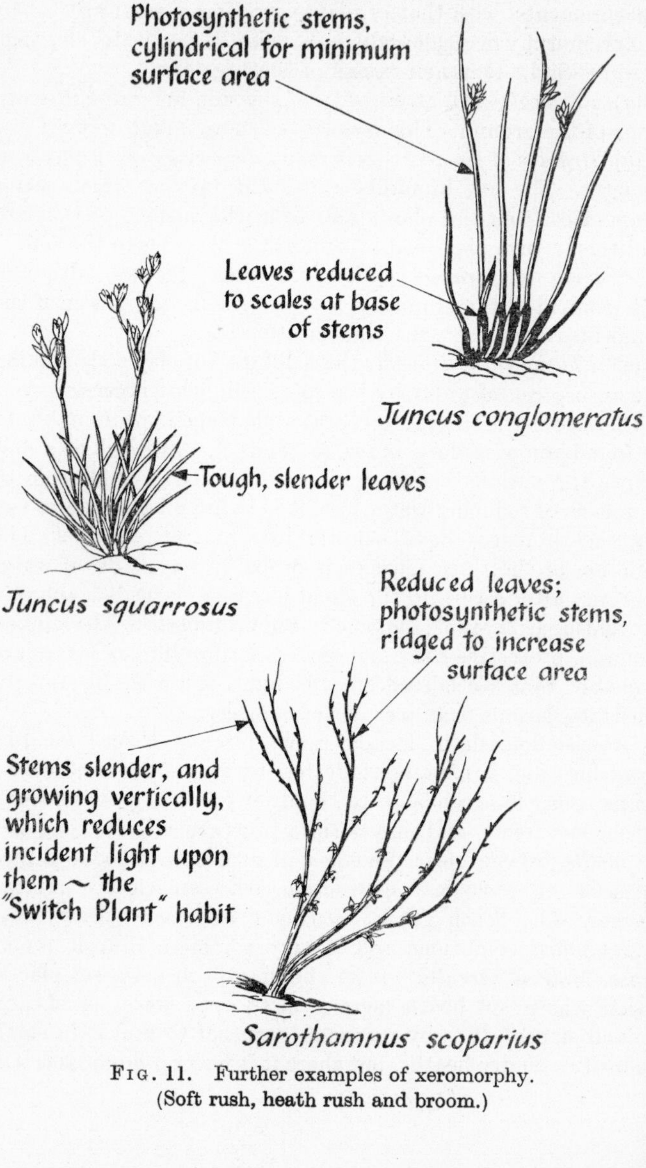

Photosynthetic stems, cylindrical for minimum surface area

Leaves reduced to scales at base of stems

Juncus conglomeratus

Tough, slender leaves

Juncus squarrosus

Reduced leaves; photosynthetic stems, ridged to increase surface area

Stems slender, and growing vertically, which reduces incident light upon them ~ the "Switch Plant" habit

Sarothamnus scoparius

Fig. 11.   Further examples of xeromorphy.
(Soft rush, heath rush and broom.)

dry heath its tussocky habit is apparent: it may be recognized at once by the many old culms which remain on the tussock (Fig. 7). Walking on these tussocks is a way of crossing marshy ground without getting wet.

Reeds grow amongst the grasses. *Juncus conglomeratus*, the soft rush, has a wide moisture range and may be found on open heath where local moisture is only very slight, but also where the soil is distinctly wet. It can also extend into standing water. On heaths its favourite habitat seems to be along ditches or the banks of streams, growing abundantly even when the bed of the stream is dry. The heath rush, *Juncus squarrosus*, grows best on the edge of wet heath—but as with so many plants any general comment about habitat is probably impossible to make, and *J. squarrosus* may grow well if not abundantly in much drier places. Sedges grow with the rushes but it would be difficult to name species which are particularly representative of dry heathland.

Heathland offers good examples of colonization and competition. The periodical summer burning destroys all the aerial parts of shrubs and minor vegetation, as well as any trees, and also scorches the surface to a variable extent. The surface, being composed of leaf litter and coarse humus, tends to burn slowly and thoroughly, so even though the A_0 and A_1 horizons may not be destroyed the habitat is greatly changed. In extreme cases the actual mineral surface, the remainder of the A_1 together with the A_2, is exposed. Most burning kills the shallow-rooted *Calluna* and also the tussock and mat-forming grasses. The *Vaccinium* however, whose rhizomes lie below the surface, generally survives, and with the advent of moisture sends up new aerial shoots, bearing 'sun' leaves. A burnt area may thus become dominated by *Vaccinium*. Subsequently *Calluna* and grasses regenerate on the burnt patch from seed blown in from outside. As the *Calluna* grows it gradually shades out the bilberry which reacts by producing 'shade' leaves and continues to grow as a subsidiary layer.

Gorse is not readily killed by fire, and on the burnt patch surrounding the remains of a bush 'seedlings' may be observed

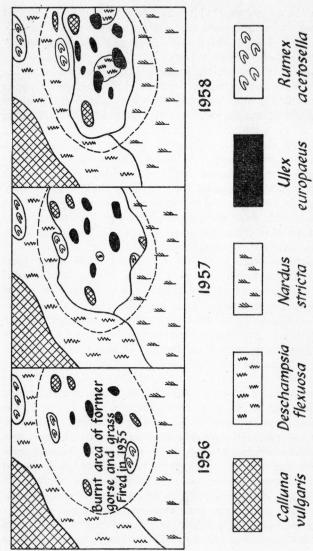

Fig. 12. Succession on a burnt patch of dry heath. The patch is two metres square.

Calluna vulgaris

Deschampsia flexuosa

Nardus stricta

Ulex europaeus

Rumex acetosella

1956   1957   1958

Burnt area of former gorse and grass. Fired in 1955

in the following year. These have probably grown from the
rootstock and are not seedlings at all.

Where bilberry does not occur burning leaves an area in
which there is virtually no vegetation, and one can then record
the succession of colonization on bare soil. A metre square can
be marked out on the bare patch and all invading plants
noted. Fig. 12 shows the succession on a patch of burnt heath.
Where *Erica cinerea* occurs with *Calluna*, burning, if sufficiently
severe, favours the *Erica* since it creates the dry conditions
which the latter prefers.

Not very much can be said about the ground flora under
Calluna heath. It depends almost entirely upon the humidity.
On dry heath some mosses may occur, but very few, e.g.
Pleurozium schreberi, Polytrichum sp. and *Dicranium* sp., while
liverworts are absent. Liverworts are never found far from
water and most of them require a substratum which is distinctly moist to the touch. Lichens, on the other hand, being
able to tolerate desiccation will grow even on the driest and
most exposed heaths, both on the leaf litter and encrusting
the stems of the dwarf shrubs, using them in fact as lichens use
the trunks of trees in woods. The greyish-green *Cladonia* is by
far the commonest, and produces an orange coloured fructi-
fication.

An acid medium inhibits the growth of bacteria, and heathland is no exception. The part played by bacteria in decay is
taken over by the saprophytic soil fungi which can tolerate
the acidity, and their hyphae exist in vast quantities in the
heathland topsoil. Some of the fungi are symbionts with the
roots of the green plants and are called mycorrhiza ('fungus-
roots'). Many kinds of plants possess mycorrhiza, probably
not all for the same reason. On heaths it would seem that
mycorrhiza in heather and young pines are associated with the
xeromorphic habit. As was pointed out above, heath plants
may not always have a low transpiration rate, but there are
certainly occasions when the physical conditions of heathland
reduce the amount of water available for passage through the
plants, and consequently reduce the intake of food substances

in solution. It has been suggested that under these conditions the covering of fungal hyphae investing the branches of the roots, and often penetrating into the cells, is able to supply the plant with water. In the case of Ericaceae this hypothesis is supported by the poor rooting systems of *Erica* and *Calluna* and by their slow rate of growth—suggesting that the plant finds that the conditions are 'difficult'. A symbiotic association confers benefit on both organisms concerned, and it is thought that in pines and other trees the fungus receives carbohydrate from the green plant, a view which is supported by the observation that the fungus does not form a covering around the roots of the young seedlings until the plants have borne foliage leaves and their roots contain excess synthesized carbohydrate (See Book List, Ref. 2.)

The lack of bacteria affects not only the process of decay but also those of nitrogen fixation and nitrate formation from humus. Nitrates are scarce in heathland soils, but it is tempting to associate the presence of endotrophic mycorrhiza (i.e. those whose hyphae actually penetrate the host's cells) with nitrogen fixation as in the root nodules of the Leguminosae. This has been claimed to occur in *Erica*, but has yet to be proved. The action of ectotrophic mycorrhiza (i.e. those whose hyphae form a sheath around the root and penetrate between the cells) is to conduct certain groups of salts, including phosphates and ammonium nitrate, from the soil water to the host. The fungal sheath may accumulate phosphate in its mycelium when there is plenty in the soil water, and release it into the host as the external concentration falls. This may help to explain why certain trees, for example, are successful colonists of poor soils, though the fact has not yet been demonstrated with pines, which are amongst the main colonists of podsols. The problem of Leguminosae growing on heaths suggests itself as suitable material for study. Herbaceous leguminous plants are not common on heaths, but gorse and broom are. The seeds of these plants should be made to germinate first in untreated heathland topsoil, secondly in this type of soil after it has been sterilized, and thirdly as a control in some light soil in which other leguminous plants are known to grow well. The seedlings should be examined periodically for growth rate and nodule development.

This book does not set out to deal with marsh or open water —these are habitats in themselves—but a few remarks on wet heath may be appropriate. The change from dry to wet heath may be gradual or very sudden. If gradual a succession will typically occur. The soil itself is generally more acidic in the wet parts—especially if they are due to soil water flowing into them from other parts of the heath rather than to rain falling upon them. The first indication of wet heath is an increase in the number of reeds, of both the soft and heath rush, and the appearance of a new species, *Juncus articulatus*, the jointed rush, so called on account of the transverse partitions along its leaves. *Erica tetralix* replaces *E. cinerea* and *Calluna*, and the grasses are almost entirely replaced by *Molinia caerulea*, which now grows closely packed so that the tussocks are less noticeable to the eye but soon discovered by the feet. Species of *Sphagnum* moss grow between the taller plants, different species in the various degrees of wetness and acidity. Bog asphodel, *Narthecium ossifragum*, and the sedge, *Eriophorum angustifolium*, or 'cotton-grass', grow here and so do many other sedges. The beaked sedge, *Rhynchospora alba*, grows in rather wetter places. Perhaps the most interesting feature of the wet heath is the presence of insectivorous plants which are not found elsewhere in the British Isles. Species of sundew, *Drosera*, bladderwort, *Utricularia minor*, and butterwort, *Pinguicula vulgaris*, all occur. The insectivorous habit does not seem to be essential to the plants' survival: they can be grown without meat, but they are then less vigorous. Although in practice insects are used as food, other pieces of protein can be 'fed' to *Drosera* and will cause the tentacles to react. Insectivory is thought to be a means of supplementing normal nutrition in soils poor in nitrates.

Heathland is a sub-climax, and except on very wet high ground (i.e. potential moorland) it tends to become pine wood. *Pinus sylvestris* is native to Britain and in addition has been

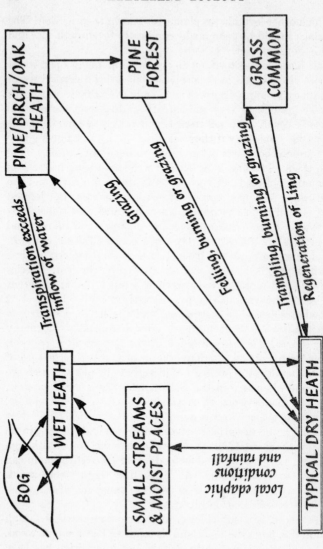

FIG. 13. Diagram to illustrate the changes which heathland may undergo as a result of the action of ecological factors.

extensively planted. It grows readily in most places, and does well on podsols because it has low calcium requirements and with the aid of its rapidly developed tap-root it obtains sufficient water. Probably the only reasons why our dry heaths do not change quickly into pine woods are the destruction of pine seedlings by rodents and by fire. The monopodial growth of pine also makes the seedlings particularly vulnerable to grazing by cattle (and to the attack of the pine-weevil) since if the leading shoot is destroyed a stunted bush spreading sideways is produced. The effect on pine of cattle grazing was known to Darwin who, in the *Origin of Species*, recorded that on a Surrey heath cattle exercised an absolute control where the pines were not protected by enclosure (see Book list, Ref. 3). In the absence of such grazing pine seedlings are very hardy, and will grow up even through shade cast by heather bushes. They then gradually shade out the heather or grass of the heath, producing pine wood, which is now to all intents and purposes the climatic climax on acidic soils, since podsolization has made the growth of deciduous forest, which *was* the climatic climax, no longer possible.

One type of heath probably *is* the natural climax, namely that which is found in exposed places near the West coast of Cornwall on soil derived from the serpentine rocks (see p. 7 and Book List, Ref. 4). In this case the very strong winds probably interfere with the growth of trees so that the dwarf shrubs are the natural dominants.

ANALYSIS

The remarks made so far are confined largely to description. Analysis on heathland is more straightforward than on other habitats and the classical methods of plant ecology, quadrats and transects, may be employed. A line transect is of use in making a qualitative study of change in environment, and is particularly valuable if soil samples are taken and analysed at intervals along it. It may be used to produce a diagram illustrating the change in vegetation from, say, swamp to pine or birch wood across an open heath, and if combined with

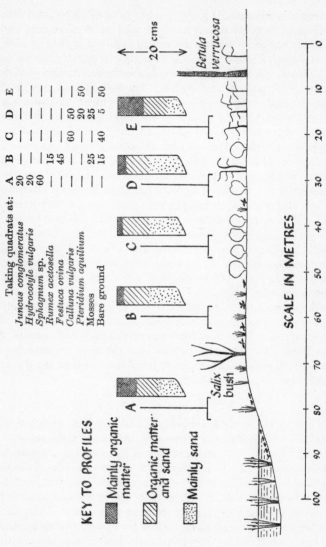

PERCENTAGE COVERAGE

Taking quadrats at:	A	B	C	D	E
Juncus conglomeratus	20	—	—	—	—
Hydrocotyle vulgaris	20	—	—	—	—
Sphagnum sp.	60	—	—	—	—
Rumex acetosella	—	15	—	—	—
Festuca ovina	—	45	—	—	—
Calluna vulgaris	—	—	60	50	50
Pteridium aquilinum	—	—	—	20	—
Mosses	—	25	—	25	50
Bare ground	—	15	40	5	—

KEY TO PROFILES

Mainly organic matter

Organic matter and sand

Mainly sand

SCALE IN METRES

FIG. 14. Line transect combined with quadrats to demonstrate succession.

quadrats can yield still more useful information. Several quadrats should be taken at random wherever there is a noticeable
change in vegetation, and a few even where no change is
apparent, just as a check. At each quadrat a soil sample,
including a pH measurement should be taken. These results
are then averaged and the averages marked at points on the
transect. Soil profiles may be drawn for each point too. In
this way a modified belt transect is made, and the use of line
and quadrat provides both qualitative and quantitative
analysis. Naturally a result such as is shown in Fig. 14 takes a
long time to obtain and is suitable for group rather than for
individual fieldwork.

A few remarks on the technique of sampling may be appropriate. The most generally useful quadrat is one made of thick
wire bent in the form of a square and welded at the joint, each
side being twenty-five centimetres long. Such a quadrat is
small enough to be carried conveniently and does not take too
long to 'work' so that several samples can be taken in a short
time. The example which follows stresses the need for taking
a large number of samples if an accurate estimate of a population is to be made; the example is botanical but the same
principle applies in estimating animal populations.

The intention here was to determine the percentage coverage
of an area of grass common which had probably been produced
as a result of heathland degenerating through rabbit activity.
The coverage was estimated by making two hundred random
throws with quarter-metre square quadrats. A random throw
is one in which the quadrat is tossed aimlessly in any direction,
a sample being taken wherever it falls. If a coloured object is
thrown instead, as a marker, fewer quadrats will be lost!
Clearly the perfect result would be obtained by placing quadrats side by side to cover the whole area; it is equally clear
that the method is impracticable for an area of any size.
Sufficient quadrats must therefore be taken to lead to a con-
sistent figure for at least the major constituents of the flora. It
will be seen from Table IV that the proportions of the dominants *Deschampsia flexuosa* and *Festuca ovina*, as yielded by

TABLE IV

Figures for the percentage ground covered by various speci
on an area of grass common, estimated after taking increasin
numbers of random samples

	NUMBER OF QUADRATS			
	50	*100*	*150*	*200*
Deschampsia flexuosa .	31·6	29·5	24·0	22·1
Festuca ovina . . .	19·1	22·6	23·4	24·4
Agrostis tenuis . . .	15·0	14·8	17·8	19·8
Rumex acetosella . .	9·1	9·0	10·4	10·6
Mosses	8·5	9·1	8·3	8·2
Holcus lanatus . . .	5·2	3·1	5·0	4·2
Nardus stricta . . .	1·2	0·7	1·0	0·6
Other species . . .	1·2	1·0	1·1	1·7
Bare ground . . .	9·1	10·2	9·0	8·4

taking only fifty quadrats, are appreciably different fror
those obtained by taking larger numbers; after the first fift
quadrats the area might have been described as a wavy ha:
grass common, whereas this grass is co-dominant with sheep'
fescue. While successive figures for coverage by the main cor
stituents show a gradual convergence towards the final valu
(e.g. for sheep's fescue 19·1, 22·6, 23·4, 24·4) this is not so for th
less numerous plants. For coverage by *Holcus lanatus* values (
5·2, 3·1, 5·0, 4·2 were obtained for the successive groups of fift
quadrats, such an irregular distribution being characteristic (
very uneven coverage. A few 'unlucky' throws may materiall
change the result. This means that, for the minor constituent

f the flora, sampling by quadrats is less reliable than it is for
he major constituents; alternatively one can say that many
nore samples should be taken before an accurate estimate of
heir coverage can be made. Quadrats are most reliable when
he various components of the flora are evenly distributed over
n area and when there are no patches of distinctive plants as
 result of very local edaphic conditions.

LIST OF DRY HEATHLAND PLANTS

This table lists the plants which are typically found, th
plants being arranged in a very rough order of abundance. Th
dotted line indicates the division between those which favour
the drier from those which favour the wetter parts, the 'dry'
plants being listed first.

The letters CF after the name imply that the plant is
strict calcifuge, i.e. it will not grow in a pH of more than
seven.

The letter K indicates that the plant is so characteristi
of heathland that its absence would be easily noticed
but it is not confined to it. In general these are plant
whose chief soil requirement is good drainage.

The letter R indicates a ruderal plant, i.e. one which may
be found over such a wide range of soil and climati
conditions that it is not characteristic of any.

SPECIES		FAMILY
Calluna vulgaris	CF	Ericaceae
Deschampsia flexuosa	CF	Gramineae
Pteridium aquilinum	CF	Polypodiaceae
		(Pteridophyta)
Galium hercynicum	CF	Rubiaceae
Potentilla erecta	K	Roseaceae
Pleurozium schreberi	CF	(Musci; Bryophyta)
Rumex acetosella	CF	Polygonaceae
Vaccinium myrtillus	CF	Ericaceae
Erica cinerea	CF	Ericaceae
Nardus stricta	CF	Gramineae
Aira praecox	K	Gramineae
Luzula campestris	K	Juncaceae
Festuca ovina	K	Gramineae
Agrostis tenuis	CF	Gramineae
Sieglingia decumbens	CF	Gramineae
Lotus corniculatus	R	Leguminosae
Ornithopus perpusillus	K	Leguminosae
Plantago coronopus	K	Plantaginaceae
Plantago lanceolata	R	Plantaginaceae
Ulex europaeus	K	Leguminosae
Sarothamnus scoparius	K	Leguminosae
Ulex minor	CF	Leguminosae

....

Salix repens	K	Salicaeae
Holcus lanatus	R	Gramineae
Juncus squarrosus	CF	Juncaceae
Erica tetralix	CF	Ericaceae
Juncus conglomeratus	K	Juncaceae
Molinia caerulea	CF	Gramineae

CHAPTER IV

THE ZOOLOGY OF HEATHLAND

THE animal life of heathland is composed of two groups, firstl
that which depends directly upon heathland plants for foo
or shelter, and secondly the much larger group which use
heathland when it provides suitable shelter but is in no wa
confined to it. No useful purpose is served by listing th
animals under these two headings, and it is preferable to begi
with a study of environmental factors.

The main biological factor is food, and shelter is linked wit
it. This is especially true of invertebrates. For the inverte
brates 'shelter' is really a composite term implying the sum
total of those physical and chemical factors which are necessar
for the animals' survival. For example, leaf litter provide
shelter for many invertebrates including springtails. Now thi
shelter is a complex of humidity, light and temperature fac
tors, which collectively provide conditions suitable for th
springtails' survival as poikilothermic* animals imperfectl
adapted to terrestrial life and liable to rapid desiccation. Th
high humidity, fairly constant temperature, and low light in
tensity are correlated with the springtails' feeding habits—
scavenging. (This is because dead organic matter tends t
accumulate in places having these physical conditions.) Thu
the springtail's shelter also leads to its food. The true insect
on the other hand, and even more the homothermic verte
brates, are less dependent upon physical and chemical factor
of their environment, so that food as such, rather than shelter
is often the limiting factor in their distribution.

* Poikilothermic animals are 'cold-blooded', that is to say their body
temperature is not maintained at a constant value by regulating
mechanisms but varies with changes of temperature in the externa
environment. Animals whose temperature varies little or not at al
with the external temperature are homothermic, or 'warm-blooded'.

PHYSICAL FACTORS. (i) HUMIDITY.

he atmospheric humidity is a factor which controls the
ctivity and therefore the distribution of many animals. It
aries greatly in different parts of the heath and certainly has
n effect on populations. Biologically the atmosphere which
natters is that in which the animals actually live, that is to
ay underneath stones, amongst grass roots, under bark, and
o on. These places are known as microhabitats within the
nain habitat which is the heath itself, and are said to possess
nicroclimates. Thus the biologist is concerned with micro-
limates of which the usual meteorological measurements give
nly a very poor indication, as is shown by the readings in
Table V.

TABLE V

Relative humidity in various situations on Headley Heath,
Surrey

SITUATION	A	B
feet above ground level on open heath .	40%	60%
At ground level among grasses . . .	45%	69%
n the A_1 horizon under grass . . .	74%	87%
At ground level under dead bracken . .	40%	62%
n the A_0 horizon under dead bracken . .	72%	85%

A: May 1958, fine hot day, air temperature 3 feet above
   ground, 16·5° C.
B: At night, corresponding air temperature 7·2° C.

In biological work the concept of saturation deficit is quite
as important as relative humidity, and will now be briefly
explained. If a free water surface is allowed to give up water
molecules to an enclosed volume of air above it, the molecules

will continue to be given up until a certain number of them is present in the volume of air. When this equilibrium is reached the air is said to be saturated, or to have a relative humidity of 100 per cent. Relative humidity is defined as the ratio between

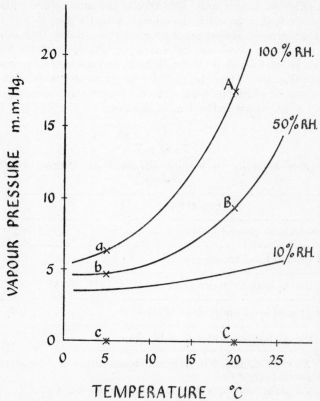

FIG. 15. Curves of the relationship between vapour pressure and temperature at constant relative humidity (R.H.).

The length AC is the saturation vapour pressure at 20° C.
The length AB is the saturation deficit at 50 per cent. R.H. at 20° C
The length ac is the saturation vapour pressure at 5° C.
The length ab is the saturation deficit at 50 per cent. R.H. at 5° C.

the weight of water vapour in a given volume of air and the weight of water vapour which the same volume of air could hold at the given temperature and pressure, expressed as a percentage. In this equilibrium individual molecules are constantly given off from the liquid state to the vapour, and a similar number of vapour molecules revert to the body of the liquid. At a given temperature, when this volume of air is saturated it contains a certain number of water molecules, and these molecules set up a pressure on account of their state of continuous motion. This is called the saturation vapour pressure, and its value varies with the temperature and pressure of the vapour above the water. The variations in atmospheric pressure do not sensibly affect vapour pressure, but daily temperature variations do have considerable effect. From Fig. 15 it will be seen that if the relative humidity is 100 per cent. then at 20 degrees Centigrade the water vapour pressure (saturation vapour pressure) is 17·51 millimetres of mercury. Now, as the temperature falls the molecular movement becomes less rapid, fewer molecules remain in the vapour state, and the vapour pressure is lowered—though the air is still holding as much water as it can; thus at 5 degrees Centigrade the saturation vapour pressure is only 6·54 millimetres of mercury.

Ecologically what matters is the drying power of the air, that is to say the rate at which water will be vaporized. Relative humidity does not tell us this even though it indicates it approximately, but has the merit of being fairly easy to measure in the field.

The rate at which water vapour will be lost from a body of liquid at a given temperature is determined by the difference between the number of molecules of water in the air at the existing humidity, and the number of molecules which saturated air could hold at that temperature. In other words the drying power of the air is better represented by the vapour pressure *deficit* or saturation deficit. Relative humidity is still useful as a shorthand expression and is easier to imagine, so that its use is permissible provided that its limitations are understood. Reference to Fig. 15 will show, by comparison of saturation deficits at different temperatures, how misleading the relative humidity alone can be as an indication of drying power over a *large* temperature range. The passage of water molecules is illustrated simply in Fig. 16 where the black dots represent water molecules.

In nature closed systems such as have been discussed do not exist. Water does not evaporate from the stomata of leaves or the respiratory surfaces of animals into a closed volume of

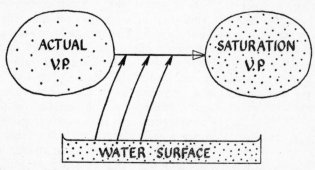

FIG. 16. Diagram to illustrate the meaning of saturation vapour pressure.

air with which it can readily establish an equilibrium. Consequently the saturation deficit may be rapidly changed, not only by changes in local temperature but even more by the sudden carrying away of the air which is in contact with the water-losing organ and which is already partly saturated. This is not brought about only by strong winds. No one who has watched an air-dispersed fruit hovering over bushes, often almost coming to rest but being suddenly carried a few inches further to one side, and then carried up again can doubt the existence of many small local air currents. Such currents deprive plants and animals of the humidity gradients which they are always building around themselves and may cause them to lose water very rapidly. This is another aspect of the inhospitable environment afforded by heathland.

Table VI

Animal counts in various situations

	AT GROUND LEVEL UNDER DEAD BRACKEN	IN THE LITTER UNDER DEAD BRACKEN	IN THE A_1 SOIL HORIZON AMONG GRASS ROOTS
Relative humidity %	40	72	74
Annelids	0	0	2
Snails	0	0	1
Slugs	0	2	1
Woodlice (*Philoscia*)	0	2	2
Spiders	3	5	1
Mites	0	4	0
Centipedes	0	6	2
Springtails	3	15	5
Earwigs	1	2	1
Carabid beetles	1	3	1
Elaterid beetles	0	1	3
Rove beetles	3	9	4
Lepidopteran pupae	0	0	3

Table VI shows the numbers of animals collected as a result of random sampling from some of the positions noted in the previous table. Samples were taken on the same day in order to obtain uniformity of conditions. The surface counts are the result of direct visual observation on the same number of quarter-metre square areas during fifteen minutes, the surface litter being very slightly disturbed. The counts in underground positions were made by shaking equal volumes of soil out on to a white-topped sorting table.

A few facts are apparent from a study of these figures:

(i) The most generally distributed animals were insects, and of these the Collembola were noticeably scarcer in one of the situations than they were in the other two.

(ii) Spiders were found on the surface as often as they were elsewhere.

(iii) Centipedes were not found on the surface.

(iv) Woodlice were scarce and not seen on the surface.

(v) Molluscs were scarce and not seen on the surface.

(vi) Annelids were very scarce.

No further comments will be made here, and the reader is left to draw his own conclusions bearing in mind the relative humidity in each situation—though humidity is certainly not the only relevant factor. He may even like to imagine how different the results might be were the samples taken under different conditions, such as at night (see the figures in Table V). He will require a torch in order to check his guesses.

The low humidity is undoubtedly partly responsible for the poor woodlouse fauna since in adjoining woodland many more individuals, especially of *Oniscus asellus* and *Porcellio scaber*, occur under the bark of decaying trees and under the leaf litter: two habitats which retain a quite high moisture content even in summer. Although a few specimens of these two species may be found on the heath it is noticeable that the number of species of woodlice occurring on the dry heath is limited, two species quite common elsewhere being rare or hard to find, namely *Armadillidium vulgare* and *Philoscia muscorum*. *Philoscia* is not plentiful near the surface though it does occur in the lower humus layers. Now woodlice are Crustacea having relatively impermeable exoskeletons impregnated with calcium carbonate, and carrying out their gaseous exchange by means of large flap-like protrusions from their abdominal appendages or pleopods. These respiratory plates are not covered with a thick integument, and on

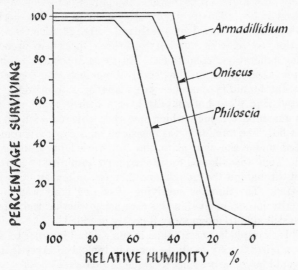

FIG. 17. Curves of the survival of woodlice at different relative humidities.

account of their large area are a constant potential source of desiccation—which is one reason why woodlice lead a retiring life, rarely venturing away from conditions of high humidity. It would seem reasonable to suppose that the absence of *Armadillidium* and *Philoscia* was due to the insufficient humidity, and experiments with *Philoscia* would support this: *Philoscia* is in fact one of the woodlice which shows least toleration of dry conditions. It would be quite wrong, however, to attribute the almost complete absence of *Armadillidium* to the same reason. *Armadillidium* is the species which resists desiccation best, and it may be found in quite exposed places with low humidity, so that clearly we must seek other reasons for its absence. The answer is probably to be found in the low calcium content of heathland soil. *Armadillidium* has a greater need of calcium than any other British wood-louse on account of its massive integument, and though it is widely distributed it is never abundant where the calcium content is low. This probably also accounts for the shortage of woodlice in general on heathland. Fig. 17 illustrates the reaction to relative humidity of three species of woodlice under laboratory conditions. This was intended to be a simple experiment of the 'survival against time' type. A constant humidity chamber was made by supporting a per-forated zinc plate horizontally over a dish of sulphuric acid in a pneumatic trough which was then covered with an air-tight lid. The humidity was measured on a paper hygrometer placed under the zinc plate and was varied by diluting the acid. Time was allowed for the required humidity to establish itself throughout the trough, and then ten animals were swiftly inserted. The number surviving after one hour was noted, the criterion of survival in this case being whether the animals were still able to move away if gently prodded.

This example has been taken in some detail in order to show how a mistake may easily be made in biological investigation. It would have been wrong to argue as follows:

> *Philoscia* and *Armadillidium* are both woodlice and have similar general structure and physiology.
> They are both scarce on heathland.
> The scarcity of *Philoscia* may be shown to be largely if not entirely due to the environment's low humidity.
> Therefore scarcity of *Armadillidium* may be assumed to be due to the same reason.

The only way of demonstrating the flaw in such 'pseudo-scientific' method is by experiment, in this case by finding out whether *Armadillidium* really does depend upon external water as much as *Philoscia*.

We shall return later to a more detailed study of edaphic features but first some further effects of humidity will be considered. Reptiles are common on heaths, amphibians very scarce. An occasional frog or newt may turn up, but these exceptions merely prove the rule: animals may always be found in the most unexpected places and such 'freak' observations are not generally of great value. Snakes and lizards, on the other hand, are characteristic of heathland, and their rustling in dry bracken or leaf litter is a familiar feature of any really warm day.

Amphibians represent a certain level of adaptation to life on land among the vertebrates, and occupy a position equivalent to that of the woodlice amongst the invertebrates. Pushing this analogy further one could bracket the insects with the reptiles, both groups having completely overcome the need for free external water (except for drinking and excretion) at any stage of their life history, and being in consequence largely adapted to land life. Being poikilothermic neither insects nor reptiles may be described as *perfectly* adapted (see page 44). The amphibians' poor lung development is compensated by cutaneous and buccal breathing. Both methods involve the release of water from large and relatively unprotected surfaces, and in addition to this the permeable skin is a constant source of water loss even when respiratory activity is low. The animal has probably very little control over this loss. Amphibians are therefore obliged to remain either in or near water, or in places where atmospheric humidity is high, though they may cross quite dry regions for a short time in travelling from one suitable habitat to another.

The main dependence of amphibians on free external water is not, however, so much in the adult condition as in the larval. It is commonplace that amphibians return to the water to breed—this is partly on account of their external fertilization and their aquatic larvae, but neither of these reasons is fundamental. Amphibians' eggs after fertilization are not covered with an impermeable membrane, and are therefore subject to desiccation in dry air. Furthermore, because of their low area-to-volume ratio (Fig. 18), and the absence of internal obstacles to diffusion in the shape of cell membranes, the eggs dry out very quickly. The egg has the same difficulty as the adult, but fewer means of overcoming it. Woodlice have exactly the same problem but meet it by keeping the eggs in a brood pouch under the thorax and then remaining in a moist atmosphere.

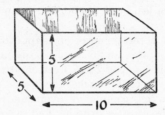

The area of this prism is 250 sq. units.
The volume is 250 cu. units.

$$\frac{\text{Area}}{\text{Volume}} = 1$$

The area of this prism is 10 sq units.
The volume is 2 cu. units.

$$\frac{\text{Area}}{\text{Volume}} = 5$$

From these figures it is clear that the smaller prism whose linear dimensions are exactly a fifth of the larger prism's has five times as much surface in relation to its volume.

The body shape of many animals approximates to that shown here— but the decrease of the area to volume ratio with increase of size applies to any shape, since area depends on the square and volume on the cube of the linear dimensions.

Fig. 18. Comparison of area and volume of two similar rectangular prisms of different dimensions.

Humidity may be measured in the field by means of Edney paper hygrometers, and a few comments on their use may be found helpful. These instruments are quite reliable if correctly used and checked for accuracy from time to time; the wet and dry bulb thermometer is certainly more accurate but not convenient for field use. If several paper hygrometers are being used they should often be placed in the same atmosphere, and then if they do not all register the same humidity they must be corrected. This may be done by determining the relative humidity using Regnault's apparatus, which calls for rather careful manipulation, or by using the wet and dry bulb thermometer, which is much easier. The hygrometers should be placed in a *gentle* draught of air which has first passed over the dry and wet bulbs of the thermometer, in that sequence; the draught must be gentle or an excessively large depression of the wet bulb will be registered. The hygrometers must be allowed at least fifteen minutes in this atmosphere before being read and adjusted. When used in the field the instrument can be suspended from bushes by means of its ring. In a breeze it may register the humidity within five minutes, but if used near the ground or in still air at least fifteen minutes must be allowed; this is its main disadvantage. Of course, when measuring microclimates one must remember that the instrument is reacting to the humidity around the coiled paper, which may not be the same as that a few centimetres away.

PHYSICAL FACTORS. (ii) EDAPHIC

Apart from its indirect influence on the fauna through the flora, soil has a direct effect on the animal population in three ways: by its chemical composition, by its texture and by its specific heat.

Characteristically there are few Mollusca and Annelida on heathland. Lack of calcium carbonate is certainly the reason for the low snail count. This is easily demonstrated by comparing the snail count in the same locality on two different types of soil, when the soil of low calcium content will be seen to support not only far fewer species but also fewer individuals. The need for calcium in shell formation is clearly the reason for this result, and of the few species of molluscs which do occur on heathland the most abundant is the slug *Agriolimax agrestis*, whose distribution is very wide. The absence of a shell is a factor which allows it to inhabit heathland. Other molluscs may spread from neighbouring woodland to the heath in wet weather. The brown-lipped snail, *Cepaea nemoralis*, is quite common: it lives on the heath itself but is not easy to find except after recent rain.

TABLE VII

Animal counts to show dependence of the various groups on environmental factors

SLOPE OF THE GROUND	North			South		
POSITION	I	II	III	IV	V	VI
Relative humidity at ground level %	68	72	72	66	61	30
pH at depth 2 inches .	6·2	7·1	7·2	6·8	4·9	4·3
Dominant flora . .	*Festuca ovina*		*Brachypodium pinnatum*		*Pteridium aquilinum*	
Annelids . . .	6	3	4	3	0	2
Molluscs . . .	23	18	18	1	4	2
Woodlice . . .	12	10	7	13	11	7
Centipedes . . .	1	1	1	2	3	1
Millipedes . . .	3	1	6	1	3	0
Spiders and mites .	7	7	1	0	3	3
Springtails . . .	9	4	7	2	1	0
Hemiptera . . .	1	1	0	0	0	0
Beetles . . .	3	1	2	2	2	3
Hymenoptera (ants) .	8	5	2	2	6	0
Dipteran flies . .	0	1	1	1	2	2

The air temperature was 16° C and a strong breeze was blowing. The bracken was dead with a few young shoots rising.

Annelids, especially the larger earthworms, are scarce in base-deficient soils but the reason for this is uncertain.

Table VII shows the result of a count made by examining the fauna amongst the roots of plants in an area of rather sudden transition from chalk down to heathland, near Dorking in Surrey. Counts were made at twenty-metre intervals by four quarter-metre square quadrats at each position. The figures given here represent the totals of all four quadrats. Certain inferences may at once be drawn from a study of these results.

The distribution of molluscs matches that of the soil's acidity, very few being found on the acid soil. The same applies to the distribution of annelids, though the total numbers found are too low to illustrate the point so nicely. The woodlice are evenly distributed in total numbers, but in fact while most of the specimens taken in the first four positions were of *Armadillidium*, few of this species were taken in the last two positions. The number of Collembola falls on the heathland, but pH is not likely to be the deciding factor in this case; the springtail count is low even in position IV which is on chalk, and the reason is probably that the springtails are avoiding the drying effect of the wind near the top of the slope, the slope itself being protected from the prevailing wind. Springtails are by no means scarce in heathland litter (see Table VI) provided that they have enough shelter. This point is discussed further on page 63. The numbers of other insects and arthropods taken are insufficient to justify general conclusions; all one can say is that on the evidence available their distribution does not appear to be controlled by either pH, or humidity, or the vegetation.

The ecological importance of the soil's specific heat was mentioned on page 6. In practice sandy soil is described as 'warm' because it is readily warmed by a comparatively brief exposure to sunlight. The reverse is also true, and so a sandy soil provides less equable conditions than, say, a clay soil. This does not matter very much in the summer when the soil temperature is never likely to be very low (not less than 12

degrees Centigrade 2 inches below the surface in Southern
England) but in the early spring it can cause insects to emerge
too soon so that they may be killed by a sudden drop in air
temperature. This is just a special case of the general feature
of heathland life, namely its great dependence on external
conditions. The low specific heat is probably a factor per
mitting the early flowering of the *Luzula campestris* or of the
gorse, and so may affect animal life, but it is almost impossible
to study such a factor in isolation; in the cases mentioned
other factors, such as lack of shade, must play a part.

Soil texture is important to animals which live in burrows
or which lay their eggs in small pits in the ground. The
carnivorous larva of the tiger beetle *Cicindela campestris*, a
characteristic heathland species, lives in a hole in the ground
where it lies in wait for passing insects which it seizes with its
mandibles and drags down to eat. The order Hymenoptera
as a whole is well represented on heaths. Ants are ubiquitous
but they thrive in loose soils. This is partly because their
method of burrowing involves carrying particles of soil, and
a heavier soil which may be either crumbly or massive depend
ing on its moisture is less easily worked.*

Many solitary wasps use the sandy ground for their burrows
the most important families being the Pompilidae or spider
hunting wasps, the Philanthidae and the Sphecidae or sand
wasps. All three families lay their eggs in burrows having
first provided food for the future larvae in the form of spiders
or insects. The solitary bees, especially of the genus *Andrena*
may be found in large numbers and are amongst the first t
emerge in spring and carry out early pollination. They ar
semi-social, several females digging their burrows close to each
other on a suitable piece of loose ground, but they are by no
means confined to heathland and occur in gardens on clay
soil, the point being that garden topsoil is generally of fine
texture because it is often disturbed.

* Earthworms, which draw the soil through their alimentary canal
are able to burrow in heavy soils (in fact they are important aerating
agents) but in the heaviest gley soils even they are scarce.

PHYSICAL FACTORS. (iii) TEMPERATURE

Temperature being one of the principal factors governing the rate of chemical reaction in general, and in particular limiting the range of enzyme action, it necessarily affects the activity of the entire organism. Activity in turn determines the ecological status of the species, and so helps to fix its distribution.

In a temperate climate the most striking effect of temperature is the way in which organisms survive the unfavourable season. Nowhere is this more apparent than on heathland, which is so largely at the mercy of climatic conditions. The ways in which animals overwinter are even more varied than those of plants; they are closely related to the animals' general structure and physiology. Clearly what is possible for a homothermic animal is not for the poikilothermic, in which rate of metabolism is intimately bound up with external conditions, especially temperature. We shall see, however, that the warm-blooded animal's independence of its environment is limited: some mammals are forced to hibernate, but of course this is due only indirectly to the effect of temperature and more often to the decrease in food supply.

Rabbits are less active in winter than in summer, but traces of them may be found above ground in the form of recent pellets even in quite cold weather. They owe their independence mainly to their constant body temperature but also to their lack of a specialized diet: the tough grasses or dwarf shrubs are always available to them, and they do not require plants in any special condition and are therefore able to feed throughout the year. This is a very important point, for it must be remembered that a constant body temperature is not just a kind of magic but that energy has to be expended in maintaining it. The reduced number of shrews may be partly explained on these lines. Shrews are not very common on heaths, but they do occur, especially near wooded places and in grass rather than heather. They are insectivorous and their potential food supply is much reduced in winter—also

they are very voracious, taking about their own body weight
of insects and other food each day—and so they go into a state
of suspended activity, using just enough energy in respiration
to keep alive. The reduction of their food supply, however, is
not their only problem. (There are *some* insects to be found
amongst the leaf litter even in winter, and the shrews, having
very keen senses, can probably find them. Slugs and especially
the woodlouse *Philoscia muscorum* are also eaten by shrews.
Shrews are very small, much smaller than mice, most of their
apparent volume being due to the thick fur; their ratio of
area-to-volume is consequently high. Now, the surface of an
animal is where heat may be lost, while the volume represents
the cells in which heat is being generated. Shrews therefore
must be active and consume prey continuously if their temperature is not to fall below that which permits them to work as
efficient co-ordinated machines. Mice, being omnivorous, do
not have quite the same problem, and in any case they have a
lower area-to-volume ratio than do the shrews. Their activity
is probably much reduced, but they too can be found in
winter. The importance of the area-to-volume ratio is illustrated in Fig. 18. But while the general principles outlined
here are true it must be admitted that the state of knowledge
about shrews, and especially about their numbers, is by no
means complete. (See Book List, Ref. 5.)

Temperature has an even greater effect on the life of
poikilothermic animals, and it is particularly well demonstrated by species which are on the fringe of their geographical
range, which applies to much of the British fauna on account
of the islands' northerly position. This kind of range limit
due to temperature must not be confused with the purely
geographical limits imposed by topographical barriers.
Amongst invertebrates and cold-blooded vertebrates evidence
of a group's being near to the limit of its range is furnished
by the paucity of its species, the small size of the species and
by life histories whose details differ from those of similar
species nearer the centre of the range. Several heathland
animals will serve to illustrate these general trends.

The Order Orthoptera, to which cockroaches and grass-hoppers belong, is very poorly represented in Britain—we have less than ten common species of short-horned grass-hoppers whereas France lists over sixty.*. They are un-doubtedly insects of warm countries, and of the short-horns it is certainly true to say that they are to be found in sunny places and avoid shade. Heaths often supply suitable con-ditions since the sandy soil is warm (see page 57) and is con-ducive to early hatching, as well as providing the adults with the right conditions. Most of our native short-horns occur on heaths, the smallest one *Myrmeleotettix maculatus* being characteristic and very common. Short-horns lay their eggs in clutches in the soil, and the nymphs which hatch out become adult between June and August, depending on the species. *Myrmeleotettix maculatus* may be found in the adult stage between July and October, but in France it can appear almost a month earlier, though the adults die off at about the same time as in Britain. Of the entire order only three British species over-winter as adults, the others over-wintering in the egg stage. In France some of the species which here over-winter as eggs survive as adults, while even further south related genera scarcely have a resting period at all but are active throughout most of the year.

Unlike grasshoppers, which are so much influenced by local temperature changes, ant colonies are little affected by the weather and a warm day in winter will see workers outside the nest, though in smaller numbers than in summer. On account of their colonial existence ants make for themselves a micro-climate which is surprisingly uniform throughout the year; the heat given off as a result of the metabolism of so many individuals raises the temperature of a nest above that of the surroundings so that it is even slightly warm to the touch.

In Britain very few Lepidoptera over-winter as adults. The small tortoiseshell butterfly and the brimstone do but they are not heathland species. While some species over-winter as larvae the vast majority take advantage of the resistant pupal

* Locusts are large short-horned grasshoppers.

stage for surviving the unfavourable season. For example some of the commonest heathland species, the small heath butterfly, *Coenonympha pamphilus*, and the common heath moth, *Ematurga atomaria*, and the cinnabar moth, *Hypocrita jacobaeae*, all over-winter as pupae. On the other hand the grayling butterfly, *Eumenis semele*, which is a characteristic heathland species over-winters as a larva, and so does the grass emerald moth, *Pseudoterpna pruinata*. These examples show how difficult it is to generalize about the habits of a large group of animals such as an order of the size of the Lepidoptera. In a large group it is unlikely that all members will be equally adapted to their environments either in structure or in behaviour, and the atypical over-wintering habits of some species reflects the evolutionary adaptation taking place in the group as a whole.

Reptiles in Britain are very close to the edge of their range and are poorly represented. The adder, *Vipera berus*, and its prey the common lizard, *Lacerta vivipara*, are characteristic heathland species and may be found during much of the year, but not in any quantity before early in May. This reveals a simple food chain whose operation is controlled largely if not entirely by temperature. The lizards feed on insects, including small beetles. Anyone who has examined leaf litter or surface soil will have noticed that beetle larvae are very numerous during the winter but that during the summer there are not many large ones. It is probably the early rise in temperature which causes many to pupate and the adults to emerge, when they become available as food for the surface-dwelling lizards; the same applies to certain dipteran (fly) larvae whose rate of development depends on temperature. Reptiles in general are much scarcer in the north and in Scotland than they are in the south, a fairly clear case of the range of large poikilothermic animals being limited by temperature. Few biological statements can, however, be made without reservations and the adder can be found right up to the Arctic circle, which is outside the range of the common lizard, its main food in this country. This illustrates the advantage of not being confined

o a single kind of food; in the far north the adder probably
eeds on nestling birds and small rodents, as it often does in
Britain.

PHYSICAL FACTORS. (iv) SHELTER

Shelter, like so many ecological factors, does not lend itself
o isolated examination; nevertheless one cannot observe a
habitat without being aware of niches which supply the requirements for various animals' modes of life, and often these niches
are formed by some physical shelter: stones, bark of trees or
leaf litter. The shelter may provide direct mechanical support
e.g. a base for spiders' webs, or birds' nests or burrows) but
often its importance lies in its humidity or temperature effects,
giving rise to microclimates favourable for small invertebrates.

On account of its open nature heathland cannot offer much
in the way of shelter to large mammals—except to burrowing
forms, especially rabbits—or to large birds. Most of these
which may use heath as a hunting ground, foxes or kestrels for
instance, are visitors from neighbouring woodland. Nests are
rarely found in isolated trees on the heath, but gorse bushes
provide suitable nesting-places for stonechats and linnets while
skylarks, amongst the most characteristic heathland species,
make their nests of the dry grass on the ground. Nightjars
make no nest at all but lay their eggs on the ground protected
by the dwarf shrubs and grasses, while the wheatears which
are characteristic summer migrants make simple nests on the
ground in hollows or disused rabbits' burrows.

Leaf litter provides shelter for large numbers of small invertebrates. They are not always easy to find because the surface
layers tend to be too dry and some of the animals withdraw to
the deeper layers. The figures quoted in Table V illustrate the
humidity variation. This leads to a layering of animals, those
having effective water-conserving mechanisms being found in
several places, while those which are imperfectly adapted to
land life must be sought either deep in the leaf litter or else
amongst grass roots where the humidity is generally higher.
Springtails bring out this point. They belong to an order of

insects, Collembola, which differs so much from the general insect type that it is often placed in a class of its own. Spring tails do not possess a tracheal system, but carry out gaseous exchange over the general body surface, the integument being quite permeable and the animals generally small. In damp weather large numbers may be found hopping on the surface of the leaf litter, but after a few warm days they must be sought further down. Small insects on the other hand, especially Hemiptera, being better adapted to land life may be found near the surface of the litter even in very dry weather. This is also true of some spiders which feed on the small insects and spring tails. The absence of tall shrubs accounts for the small number of orb-web spinning spiders found on heaths. These spiders catch flying insects in their webs, and although the bracken is tall enough for the orb-webs to be spread out it is often so thick that insects do not fly readily in it. Some orb-webs may, however, be found around the edges of bracken clumps or on gorse bushes.

Far more typical of the heathland are the jumping spiders (Salticidae) and the wolf spiders (Lycosidae) which spin no web but pursue their prey on the ground, the former leaping at it and the latter running it down with fast movements. Spiders are able to resist desiccation, and may be found running about on the surface of leaf litter even in dry weather. They some-times occur in such great numbers that if disturbed, especially on a hot day when they are active, they make a characteristic rustling sound on the dry leaves. Of the jumping spiders *Evarcha arcuata* is commonly found running over the heather bushes, while the wolf spiders *Arctosa perita* and *Trochosa terricola* are characteristic species; the latter forms the prey of the spider-hunting wasp *Anoplius fuscus*, a good heathland food relationship (page 69).

Some web spinning spiders make use of the low vegetation for spreading webs in which they trap walking or low-flying insects. The Linyphiidae spin hammock-webs consisting of a horizontal platform made steady by a few threads anchored to the ground. The platform itself may be supported by such

FIG. 19. Types of spiders' webs.

small plants as *Rumex acetosella* or low growing grasses, and i
is these webs which are so easily seen when covered in dew bu
are generally overlooked at other times. Linyphiid spiders are
mostly very small. The Theridiidae make larger webs which
consist of a number of threads stretched more or less vertically
between two supports such as branches of *Calluna* or *Ulex*. The
threads cross in all directions and low-flying insects may be
caught in them. Webs are illustrated in Fig. 19.

The point to note here is that the four families of spiders
mentioned are by *no* means confined to heathland (the Linyphiidae and Theridiidae can build their webs on tall vegetation
too) but because of the kind of shelter afforded by heathland
they are characteristic species. An interesting piece of fieldwork is to examine the prey caught in various kinds of web and
to relate it to the spiders' mode of life; this will bring out what
is meant by an 'ecological niche'.

Another effect of the lack of tall shelter is that wind is keenly
felt on heathland (page 1), and this affects the larger flying
insects. Hymenoptera, generally strong fliers, are characteristic
and responsible for much of the insect pollination, but the less
powerful moths are not so plentiful. Clearly it is unlikely that
a lepidopteran, whose larvae are so often confined to one or
two food plants, will prosper if the adults are in danger of
being blown right away from the food plant. Many small
lepidoptera having poor powers of flight also live on heathland but they do little more than fly around the clumps of
heather.

The importance of the wind is brought out by the large
number of plants which do not rely on insects for their pollination but are anemophilous and have wind-dispersed fruits.
This is in striking contrast to the condition prevailing in
woodland where, apart from the trees, most of the plants are
entomophilous and animal dispersed fruits are common. It is
significant that *Calluna* may be pollinated both by insects and
by the wind.

BIOTIC FACTORS. (i) FOOD RELATIONSHIPS

It is a commonplace that 'all flesh is grass.' Most animals feed directly on plants and a much smaller number of carnivores prey on these herbivores.

The open nature of heathland obliges most of its animals to live in close proximity, and this makes the task of unravelling the relationship between the species rather difficult. Every species has a place in a food chain but close neighbours may not in fact be members of the same food chain; for example ants, ladybirds, aphids and weevils may all occur on the same gorse bush, but their activities are quite distinct. The aphids feed on the young growth of the gorse, the ladybirds and their larvae prey on the aphids, while the ants draw honeydew from them, and the weevils may lay their eggs in the developing gorse fruit.

Often a food chain is obvious—as when we see a spider kill and feed on a fly which it has caught in its web. The prey of the carnivorous mammals, or birds, or snakes, can be identified by examining the contents of the predator's gut or faeces, which leads to a fairly definite conclusion (see Book list, Ref. 6). This method is scarcely possible in the case of small invertebrate predators, and here it is generally necessary to carry out a simple test of what food the animal will accept. For this purpose the suspected predator is best kept in a transparent perspex box with a tightly fitting lid and having the bottom lined with moist filter paper. Several of the suspected prey are then introduced into the box, which is periodically examined; if the number of introduced animals gradually decreases, and no entire dead bodies can be found, it is reasonable to suppose that the missing animals have been eaten. This method could be used to determine, for instance, whether centipedes prey on springtails, but one must be quite clear as to what such an experiment really shows. Supposing that after four days all the springtails were still alive—this could mean among other things that:

(a) the springtails were not acceptable as food, or

(b) the springtails were able to escape very easily in the free space of the box, or

(c) the springtails were too large or the centipede too small, or

(d) the centipede used may have been slightly damaged in capture and not be behaving naturally.

Still more possibilities will occur to the reader. Clearly, then, a negative result to this sort of experiment is wholly unsatisfactory. Now, supposing that the number of springtails *had* decreased, while the centipede remained active. One must *not* conclude from this that 'centipedes prey on springtails'. This test has merely shown that one individual of a certain species of centipede preyed on certain species of springtail under the given experimental conditions. Repetition with more centipedes of the same species may show that preying on springtails is characteristic of this species under certain quite arbitrary conditions of captivity. This might be because:

(a) this really *is* what happens in nature, or

(b) the springtails were eaten because no other food was available, or

(c) the springtails had no concealment such as leaf litter, or

(d) the species were close together but in nature might occupy different zones in the humus.

Experiments should then be devised which eliminate all the possibilities other than (a), but care must be taken not to introduce a third factor into the investigation. For instance, supposing we were trying to show that springtails were eaten only in the absence of more acceptable food, one could offer the predator some mites at the same time as the springtails. Decrease in number of the mites could be due to their having been eaten by the springtails and not by the centipede at all. This would call for a straight check of springtails-with-mites before any valid conclusion could be reached as to the centipede's behaviour.*

* It is no part of the author's intention to reveal whether or not centipedes may prey on springtails or mites or vice versa. The reader will, no doubt, wish to find out for himself.

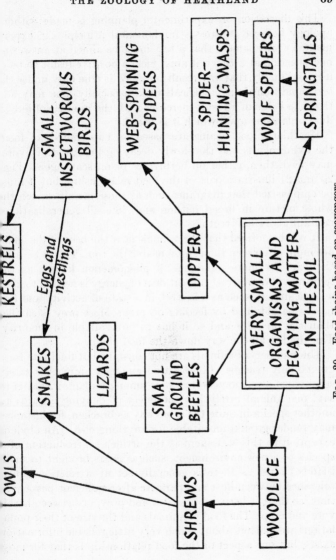

Fig. 20. Food chains based on scavengers.

This digression on experimental planning is made withou apology because it stresses fundamental principles in exper mental work, namely that a test must be aimed at answerin one question at a time: it must yield a positive result to be o use, and finally that any result obtained is true only under th test conditions. In biological work, especially, one may ad that the value of a result increases with the number of indivi dual organisms upon which it is based.

Heathland food chains are based on two sources of food the living plants and the slowly decaying humus. Carnivore may feed, then, either on herbivores or on scavengers. Figs 20 and 21 illustrate part of the food relationship, but it mus be emphasized that diagrams such as these merely sketch th whole picture in broad outline and, like all generalizations contain many half-truths.

It will be noticed that the animals near the base of the chai are more often seen than those nearer the top. This is becaus they are far more numerous, a phenomenon known as th 'pyramid of numbers'. A great deal of energy is needed to kee a large animal, such as a kestrel, in a state of activity and thi has to be obtained by feeding on prey. Most prey is smalle than the predator and so it has to be available in quantity This applies all the way down the food chain.

The numbers of animals are not constant but fluctuate for a great many reasons. Competition amongst animals is rarel so obvious a phenomenon as it is amongst plants: that is to say, one animal rarely has the effect of denying an area to another species in quite the same way as bracken, for instance may render ground unsuitable for anything else. (An obviou exception to this statement is the artificial introduction of a species to a new environment, such as goats brought to smal islands.) Just as there is generally set up a relationship o tolerance between host and parasite after sufficient passage o time, so there is between predator and prey, or between herbi vore and crop. The food of animals and the size of their popu lations are matters about which very little reliable informatio exists, but one aspect of the food relationship is that for mos

PLATE V

A Lycosid wolf spider. A female carrying her egg cocoon. The specimen is photographed against a light background for clarity; if it were placed on its natural background it would be difficult to see.

PLATE VI

Two animals at the top of the pyramid of numbers, or at the end of the food chains. The kestrel's large eyes, placed well forward, give it both a wide field of view and a large area of binocular vision which is necessary for an animal which pounces on its prey. The adder owes its success as a predator partly to its cryptic coloration which is not seen to advantage against the background shown here. It has its head raised about to strike.

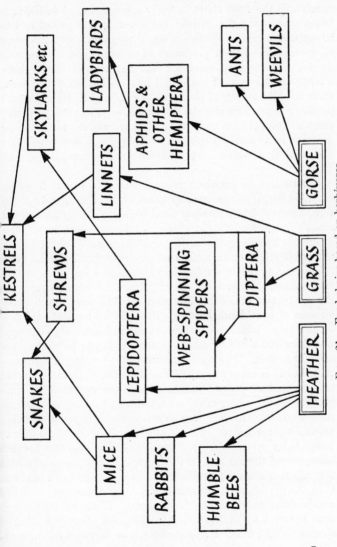

Fig. 21. Food chains based on herbivores.

carnivores the food chain is fairly specific, i.e. in addition to being able to say that shrews eat woodlice it is probably true to say that a certain species of shrew preys on a certain species of woodlouse—in fact predators of different species probably do not compete very much for food but keep rather to themselves. In the case of nocturnal hunters this may be due to their not all hunting at the same time of night. Rarely does a predator depend on one species exclusively, but it has 'preferences'. Competition may arise if there should be a sudden decrease in a species' preferred food, in which case it will take a second best which may decrease another predator's main supply.

Fluctuation in numbers is more likely to occur, however, amongst herbivores, especially those which, like most Lepidoptera, are restricted in their food plants. The grass emerald moth's larva feeds upon gorse and broom, and in an area where the bushes had been destroyed by fire it would not breed though it might enter from another area. Similarly the grayling butterfly feeds on heather nectar and its larva on the heath grass, *Aira praecox*. Clearly fire which would long delay the production of heather flowers would also keep graylings off an area of heathland, because although the larvae could feed on the *Aira*, which soon regenerates, it is unlikely that eggs would be laid there by adults which would not be visiting the area for nectar. This is an example of fluctuation in a population, but it is hardly competition since the butterflies are not competing with other animals. Conditions approaching competition occur when rabbits on *Calluna* heath graze around their warrens. This has been shown to result in the production around a large warren of belts of plants in increasing order of palatability to rabbits (see Book list, Ref. 7), the heather being forced further and further away. In this case the rabbit is competing against many insects which depend upon heather. Competition between animals could occur as a direct result of competition amongst the food plants. If an area of heath were invaded by mat-grass, then the population of feathered Gothic moths, *Tholera popularis*, whose larvae feed on mat-grass, might slowly increase, and as the grass gradually replaced the heather there would be less and less nectar available for the adult Lepidoptera of other heather-feeding species.

BIOTIC FACTORS.
(ii) POLLINATION AND DISPERSAL

As might be expected many heath plants are wind-pollinated, and these show all the usual features. Of those which are insect-pollinated the majority rely on bees, especially humble bees, and this is no doubt due to the insects' powerful flight which is not readily interrupted by the wind. Commonly occurring species are the heath humble bee, *Bombus jonellus*, and the large red-tailed *Bombus lapidarius*, while the hive bee visits ling heather. All members of the Ericaceae as well as gorse and broom are adapted for insect pollination, and some details of their mechanism are illustrated in Fig. 22.

Most heathland species make use of the wind for dispersal of their fruits—all the grasses for instance produce light fruits which are easily carried, while the *Rumex acetosella* has projections from its fruit which assist in wind dispersal. Gorse pods dehisce and in so doing fling the seeds a little way, so that although they are heavy the wind may help by pushing them a little further, and this is another reason why small gorse bushes grow around the parent plants. The noise made by a big gorse bush during dehiscence is quite noticeable; the seeds can then be further dispersed by ants (see page 25). Not many fruits are dispersed principally by animals; *Vaccinium* produces a succulent berry which is an important food for grouse on heather 'moors'.

An interesting study of the effect of animal activity on distribution can be made by using the fruits of oak trees. Solitary oaks often grow on heath as part of the ecological succession (Fig. 13) and a large tree will in a good year drop a great many acorns uniformly on every side, most of the tree's fruits falling within a fortnight. An approximate figure for the total crop is obtained by counting the acorns on part of the tree and making the appropriate multiplication; the work is made

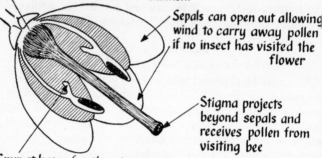

Nectar secreted near base of filament

Sepals can open out allowing wind to carry away pollen if no insect has visited the flower

Stigma projects beyond sepals and receives pollen from visiting bee

Spur at base of anther increases likelihood of pollen being brushed on bees proboscis by tilting the anther

Calluna ~ view with one sepal and two petals removed; only two stamens are shown

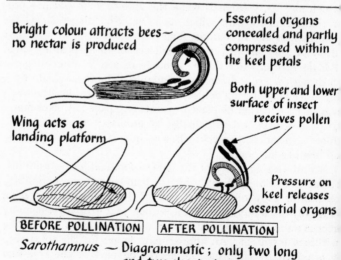

Bright colour attracts bees— no nectar is produced

Essential organs concealed and partly compressed within the keel petals

Both upper and lower surface of insect receives pollen

Wing acts as landing platform

Pressure on keel releases essential organs

BEFORE POLLINATION   AFTER POLLINATION

Sarothamnus ~ Diagrammatic; only two long and two short stamens are shown

FIG. 22. Pollination mechanisms.

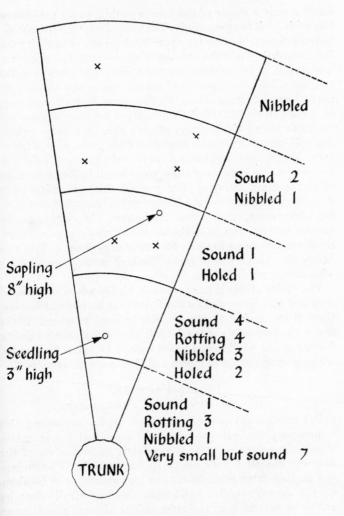

FIG. 23. Record of an acorn survey. The lines drawn across the sector are at 5-yard intervals.

easier if only a sector of the tree is worked at a time—henc
this lends itself to group study. The ground near the tree shoul
be carefully searched for very young oak saplings and their posi
tion recorded. Then the number of acorns and their conditio
(unharmed, holed, nibbled, etc.) at various distances from th
tree are noted over a period of several weeks, the acorns onc
noted being left in position. Fig. 23 shows how a record ma
be made. In the outer belts where there are fewer acorns it i
useful to record the position of each one. A survey such a
this will make it clear why abundant fruit production is neces
sary. Very few of the acorns will ever take root and if the sur
vey can be continued over a few years it will be found that fe
of the seedlings survive. The gradual drift of acorns awa
from the tree points to some kind of animal dispersal, and care
ful observation may reveal its nature. Woodpigeons ar
agents, rabbits may push the acorns as they run about, anc
small rodents using them as food may drag them a little wa
before dropping a few of them. Baiting small mammal trap
with acorns can help here.

The fruits of birch trees, though highly adapted for win
dispersal may be carried on the feathers of finches which some
times flock around the ripe catkins in large numbers. If th
fruits can pass safely through their alimentary canals this is
further means of dispersal but it cannot be taken for grante
without examination of faeces and then a germination test.

BIOTIC FACTORS.
(iii) COLOUR AND CAMOUFLAGE

In every habitat most of the animals are inconspicuous; thi
is necessary for both predators and prey, and the extent t
which the concealment is successful is an indication of th
animal's overall adaptation to its environment. Camouflag
is a matter either of matching the background or of breakin
up the animal's outline—and while this is generally done b
colour or pattern (e.g. the green colour of some grasshopper
matches the grass) in some cases the shape of the animal play
a part (e.g. some caterpillars have knobs on their bodies whic

make them resemble the twigs on which they rest). Features which help in concealing the stationary animal are called 'cryptic'. There are also examples of 'flash' coloration such as the yellow underwing moths, *Triphaena* sp., whose bright orange hind-wings are quickly folded on landing; this sudden disappearance of the colour probably confuses a pursuer who is 'looking' for something orange.

The small number of species in the heathland flora leads to uniformity of colour, and hence the cryptic coloration of heathland animals tends to be somewhat similar; greys and browns predominate to match the heather and the grasses which even when fresh are greyish rather than bright green. A convincing study of the effectiveness of cryptic coloration can be made using grasshoppers and small boys who know nothing about the subject. Two areas of heath should be selected, one of which is a brighter green than the other. The boys are then told to catch all the grasshoppers they can on each patch in turn, in a given time, and the catch from each area is kept alive and separate. The grasshoppers will reveal themselves by movement and their characteristic noise (stridulation). It will be found that on the 'dark' area the ratio of brown individuals to green ones is high, and on the 'light' area the reverse is true;* in fact none of the 'wrongly coloured' insects may be found at all. On being told to repeat the search, this time taking great care and making a point of *looking* for the dark grasshoppers on the dark patch, and vice versa, still more will probably be found. This means that the cryptic coloration of the brown and of the green grasshoppers on their matching backgrounds was successful, and this experiment using boys as predators is valid because the birds which are the usual predators are, like the boys, sensitive to sound and, unlike most mammals have colour vision. If the green grasshoppers are now released on the dark patch and vice versa the boys will be able to catch the same numbers as before in far less

---

* The brown grasshoppers may be either all of one species or dark coloured specimens of species whose colour varies. It is the colour which matters for the present purpose and not the species.

time, showing even more clearly that cryptic coloration is a very valuable adaptation. These tests could mean either that grasshoppers of the 'wrong' colour are quickly killed off and so in nature are not plentiful, or else that grasshoppers are sensitive to background colour and not many wander to the 'wrong' background. The reader will, no doubt, wish to devise a simple choice experiment for himself in which grasshoppers of various colours are offered a choice of several different backgrounds. Adult grasshoppers are most plentiful in late August and September but the experiment can be tried with nymphs. A necessary precaution in the experiment described above is to take fairly large areas of green or brown background; small patches are not desirable because a grasshopper may have landed temporarily on the 'wrong' patch, perhaps even on account of the activity of the experimenters, and then the experiment will have failed.

The grayling butterfly shows remarkable cryptic coloration on the underside of its hind-wings, which are greyish-brown and a good match with the heathland soil. When resting the whole body is tilted towards the sun so that the least possible shadow is cast: a shadow of course cannot match a background in the same way as a pattern and often betrays the animal which casts it. The grayling tucks its fore-wings between the hind-wings when resting with its wings folded, and so conceals a prominent eyespot on the underside of the fore-wing. When feeding, as opposed to merely resting, the butterfly may well be more exposed, and then it reveals its fore-wing. Predatory birds probably aim for this false target and the butterfly escapes with little more damage than the loss of some of its wing area.

In the larva of the emperor moth, *Saturnia pavonia*, we see a further case of suiting the colour to changing conditions. At first the larvae are very dusky and of one colour, which is satisfactory protection amongst the heather twigs but, as pointed out above, large patches of black are rather noticeable. When the larvae grow larger they change to a green colour relieved with reddish spots which gives better concealment, though if examined outside their environment they look gaudy.

The birds which prey on insects are themselves coloured as a protection against the chief predator, the kestrel. Skylarks are perhaps amongst the most characteristic insectivorous birds on heathland. While in general the bird is brown there is plenty of white to break up the uniformity. Most animals are darker above than below in order that their backs, which receive more light, may not appear very much lighter than the underparts. Wheatears are a good example of this general rule ; in a stuffed specimen the contrast between the blue-grey head and back and the nearly white under parts is great, but from some distance away on the heath they are inconspicuous even though they are not small birds.

Adders with their brown and buff markings are well protected, and so are lizards. For such ground-dwelling species a dark colour relieved by a little white is a good match against the dark heathland humus, which is generally broken up into small patches of grey by dead heather twigs or the shiny bases of the tough grasses. Wolf spiders often have black and white striping, which is excellent camouflage when stationary but much less effective when running. They are easily caught if chased to a green patch.

Some animals, chiefly insects, seem to use the very reverse of cryptic or flash coloration and are conspicuously coloured the whole time. Examples of these are the adult ladybirds, nearly all species of which are a brilliant red or yellow with contrasting black patterns, and the larvae of the cinnabar moth which feed semi-gregariously on ragwort and are brilliantly coloured with circular bands of black and orange along their entire length. Clearly they cannot hope to escape detection, but few of them are eaten by birds. Their colouring is called aposematic, or warning, and the vivid colour is accompanied by some unpleasant feature—taste in the examples quoted, or in the case of wasps a painful sting. After a few attempts young birds learn (the word 'learn' is strictly correct) to leave such prey alone. This device enables the ladybirds to feed on aphids at their leisure in exposed places, indeed they are not able to move fast. The two-spot ladybird, *Adalia bipunctata*, is very common and so is the small light yellow *Thea vigintiduopunctata* which has twenty-two minute black spots. Where there are pine trees the large *Anatis ocellata* will probably be found.

A final example of protection is the way in which the bee-moths, *Hemaris* spp., and bee-flies imitate humble bees not only in having large furry bodies but also in their manner of flying (see Book list, Refs. 8 and 9). The insects are very difficult to tell apart in the air. It is thought that resemblance to stinging insects (birds learn to avoid humble bees) protects the moths and flies which do not have such means of defence. Clearly the device is useful only if the mimics are far less numerous than the models, as the humble bees are called, for if this were not so birds could not learn to avoid the models. Bee-moths occur on heaths but for the reasons mentioned are not often seen and still more rarely recognized.

NOTES FOR TEACHERS

SUGGESTIONS FOR CLASS PRACTICAL WORK

The following comments are suggestions as to how heathland may be used in teaching ecology to beginners. The author has always viewed the 'teaching of teaching' with scepticism and does not propose to add to the literature on that subject. These notes are merely an outline of a course which has been suitable in the conditions under which the author has worked: there is nothing dogmatic about them, and this is the spirit in which they are offered to other teachers.

It is best to start about the middle of a summer term, and to have an area of woodland nearby for purposes of comparison. Six two-hour sessions can give an enthusiastic pupil enough background to continue studying on his own.

Session I. *A demonstration of physical and chemical factors*

Comment on the open nature of the habitat; the effect of wind, cloud and sun can be felt. Measure the air temperature and humidity and compare it with that of woodland. Examine the soil for texture; sand particles and humus show up clearly with the hand lens. Measure the humidity below ground level. Then show the soil's acid reaction by means of Universal Indicator. (All that is necessary is a bottle of indicator and one of distilled water, and a saucer. It is a good idea to bring a small tube of acid and one of alkali too to demonstrate a control on the indicator before testing the soil. This could be done beforehand in class but it is rather effective in the field.) Finally, the class can learn to identify a few of the characteristic plants.

Session II. *The botany of the habitat*

A quick revision of the plants already studied is followed by the pupils themselves making collections of the plants

81

which they think are representative. On bringing the specimens back a distinction can be drawn between calcifuge,
characteristic and ruderal. This should yield many of the
species listed on page 43. A brief discussion of the features
common to the typical heathland species should then be held,
correlating the features as far as possible with the physical
conditions of the habitat.

Session III. Competition

On a piece of ground where competition is evident quadrats
should be taken at suitable positions, in order to show quanti-
tatively how one species encroaches on another or exploits a
burnt patch better than others. If possible this should be
repeated on different patches where burning occurred two
years and several years before, in order to bring out the idea
of succession.

Session IV. The zoology of the habitat

This is best done in warm dry weather when there are plenty
of insects on the wing. Look for birds in flight and on the
ground, also for their nests. Draw attention to the small
number of species of birds and to the fact that they are not
the same as those in the woodland. Then distribute specimen
tubes and let the pupils collect as many animals as they can,
taking care to include a piece of the plant or soil on which the
animal was found. (It is quite essential to have plenty of
tubes available: sharing is useless.) When this is done the
specimens should be named, if possible, down to families in
insects and orders in the case of most other arthropods.
Pupils must make lists in their notebooks, on the spot, of the
animals' names and relative abundance. If time permits the
class can then be shown how to obtain many more animals
from a small area by suitable collecting methods.

Session V. Pollination and dispersal

The class should list from its own observations as many
examples of wind and animal pollination and dispersal as it

can. The observations should then be correlated with the physical conditions of the habitat. This session is very useful for revising the plant identification previously studied.

Section VI. Further examples of plant and animal interaction

This calls for a little classroom instruction beforehand. The pupils in the field cannot be expected to make much of this topic on their own and the session is best taken as a conducted tour. (It should also be used as an opportunity for revising the animals previously observed.) It should be possible to demonstrate much of the information concerning food chains which is shown in Figs. 20 and 21; suitable material would be springtails, small Diptera, various kinds of spider, a lizard, insectivorous birds, mouse runs, rabbit faeces, hawks. Close study of a gorse bush may reveal weevils, ants, aphids and ladybirds (probably all stages of ladybird life-history). Examples of cryptic and aposematic coloration will be evident.

A HEATHLAND DIARY

The brief records given here are edited from actual observations and are intended to indicate the changes in activity which take place from month to month. They will serve to give some idea of what a beginner may look for, but are in no way exhaustive.

January

The fronds of bracken, and oak and birch leaves, showed little sign of decomposition. Gorse was out of flower. There was abundant new growth of heath bedstraw and sheeps' sorrel, especially where small hollows (e.g. old rabbit burrows) provided shelter. Examination of humus in situ revealed no animals, but on bringing a sample from a depth of five centimetres indoors a few mites and springtails emerged after a few hours' warmth. Fresh rabbit droppings were plentiful, even at a distance of a hundred yards from the nearest burrows in very cold weather.

February

Decomposition had still not progressed noticeably. The leaf tips of the heath rush were brown, possibly as a result of frost damage. The heath bedstraw was growing well, and also the sheeps' sorrel, the latter using as shelter the matted dead leaves of Yorkshire fog. Grasses showed no sign of new growth, with the occasional exception of sheeps' fescue and wavy hair-grass. A very little new growth of ling was seen under the shelter of parent plants.

Webs of Linyphyiid spiders were found in good condition, but the spiders were not seen. Rabbit droppings were plentiful and there was much recent burrowing in the sand.

March

Sheeps' sorrel was growing well in the places previously noted, and the new growth of wavy hair-grass was evident, especially on burnt patches. Ling had progressed little. Common oak buds showed no sign of activity although in sheltered woodland nearby they were beginning to swell. Gorse blossom was plentiful, even after a long cold spell. The emergence holes of semi-colonial bees were revealed by numerous small heaps of loose sand. Seven-spot ladybirds were plentiful on the gorse, but not active. Skylarks, starlings and field-fares were seen.

April

Field woodrush was in full bloom early in the month, and towards the end the first few flowers of dwarf gorse appeared. The humus and litter fauna was plentiful, examination revealing several earwig nymphs as well as beetle larvae, small spiders and woodlice. A few tiger beetles were on the wing late in the month and at the same time common lizards were active and often seen.

May

The inflorescences of wavy hair-grass and sheeps' fescue were formed but had not opened out, while in one or two places mat-grass was beginning to flower. The heath rush inflorescences were only five centimetres high by the end of the month. Ribwort plantain, tormentil and sheeps' sorrel were in flower, the last shedding abundant pollen at the lightest touch. The cottony wind-dispersed seeds of creeping willow were being released in great quantity. Few flowers of the common gorse remained.

Lycosid spiders were abundant, and in the latter half of the month some females were carrying cocoons. At the same time nymphs of grasshoppers were abundant on mat-grass. On the ling were found the heather beetles *Lochmaea suturalis* and under it, in the litter, the larvae of many carabid ground beetles and elaterids (click beetles). Two and seven-spot lady-birds were caught in flight, and around the ling were flying some small heath butterflies, small moths and the homopteran bug *Ulopa reticulata*. Skylarks were flying high and singing; a pair on the ground ran around in an agitated manner and flew short distances when the observers approached their nest. Swallows were flying, skimming low over the ling.

June

Many plants were flowering including wavy hair-grass, mat-grass, tormentil and sheeps' sorrel. The sheeps' sorrel had formed many fruits by the end of the month. The purple moor grass inflorescences were forming but had not extended. Many seedlings of birch and oak appeared in leaf, having developed from the previous year's seed.

Wolf spiders were very numerous, many carrying cocoons. On bringing some back to the laboratory the young hatched out and could be seen clinging to the females' backs. The nymphs of grasshoppers were still active on mat-grass and also on ling. Small heath butterflies, dragon flies and ladybirds were seen in flight. There was cuckoo spit (nymphs of cercopid bugs) on many plants including sheeps' sorrel. Lizards were plentiful. Skylarks were flying high, singing, and wheat-ears were feeding on the ground but were not easy to approach.

July

The plants which flowered in June were still in flower, and ir addition the white flowers of heath bedstraw were con spicuous. Common bent grass, *Agrostis tenuis*, and heath rush flowered throughout the month.

Adults of the grasshopper *Myrmeleotettix maculatus* appeared about the middle of the month, and the first adults o *Omocestus viridulus* and *Chorthippus parallelus* towards the end. Many queens of the large red-tailed humble bee were seen. Gorse weevils were abundant on gorse flowers and so were ants and aphids. A large flock of social finches, including redpolls, spent many hours visiting the birch *Betula verrucosa* apparently feeding on the ripened fruits. They flew off when approached but only a short distance, and then settled again Rabbits were active at most times of the day.

August

Most of the plants which bloomed in June and July were still in flower in the early part of the month. Ling was in full bloom throughout, and so was common gorse, but even at the beginning some of its fruits were already dehiscing noisily Towards the end of the month few flowers of heath bedstraw remained.

This was the best month for insects generally. In place where springtails had been numerous earlier in the year they were much scarcer near the surface. The rich surface inverte brate fauna included spiders, earwigs, cockroaches (*Ectobiu pallidus*) and ants, while dung beetles were plentiful on a patch where sheep were allowed to graze. Scorpion-flies flev weakly among the ling. Hive bees were amongst the mos numerous insects flying near the ling, while the gorse wa visited chiefly by humble bees.

September

Ling and purple moor grass were still in flower, the webs o many Linyphyiid spiders being found on the ling. All th grasshoppers previously noted were still active, but by the end

PLATE VII

Nightjar sitting on its 'nest' which consists largely of dried remains of bracken fronds—a good example of cryptic coloration.

PLATE VIII

Grayling butterfly, showing the large eyespot on the forewing and cryptically coloured hind middle-wing. For explanation see p. 78.

of the month only *Myrmeleotettix maculatus* remained in any abundance. Other active insects included crane-flies (Tipulidae), hover-flies (Syrphidae), humble bees, many micro-lepidoptera and homopteran plant bugs. Common lizards were harder to find by the end of the month.

October

A few flowers of common gorse remained, some bitten through the calyx and others through the standard petal. Many seven-spot ladybirds were found inactive near the tips of gorse twigs. A platform web was in use and had remains of small flies on it. A few Linyphiid spiders were seen until late in the month.

November

This was the least eventful month of the year.

December

Common gorse flowered intermittently throughout the month. Cold and windy weather did not deter rabbits and their fresh faeces were found.

BOOK LIST

The works which have a reference number prefixed are those to which the reader is referred in the text. The others are of general interest.

1. Correspondence on 'Chalk Heathland.' *Nature*, July 7th, 1956 and March 9th, 1957.

2. BRIERLEY, J. K. 'Plant Symbiosis.' *School Science Review*, June, 1957.

3. DARWIN, C. *The Origin of Species*, Chapter III.

4. COOMBE, D. F. and FROST, L. C. 'The Heaths of the Cornish Serpentine.' *Journal of Ecology*, 44, No. 1, 1956.

5. CROWCROFT, P. *The Life of the Shrew*. Max Reinhardt, 1957.

6. SANKEY, J. *A Guide to Field Biology*. Longmans, 1958.

7. THOMPSON, H. and WORDEN, A. *The Rabbit*. Collins New Naturalist, 1956.

8. FORD, E. B. *Moths*. Collins New Naturalist, 1955.

9. IMMS, A. D. *Insect Natural History*. Collins New Naturalist, 1947.

The *Guide to Field Biology*, No. 6 above, should be read by all who are interested in ecology. It contains a very full and helpfully annotated bibliography.

HALL, A. D. *The Soil*. John Murray, 5th Edition, 1947. Although no longer quite up to date this book is a first-class example of the entire subject lucidly explained, and for this reason is preferable to some more recent books.

ROBINSON, G. W. *Soils, their Origin, Constitution and Classification*. Allen & Unwin, 1949. More up to date than Hall and not too difficult.

TANSLEY, A. G. *The British Islands and their Vegetation*. C.U.P., 1953. This is the standard work on British plant ecology.

TANSLEY, A. G. *Britain's Green Mantle*. Allen & Unwin, 1949. A very readable general account.

LEACH, W. *Plant Ecology*. Methuen, 1949. One of Methuen's Monographs. Very useful as an introduction.

ELTON, C. *Animal Ecology*. Sidgwick & Jackson, 1927. This, again, is a classic and should be read for its own sake even though there are more recent books. The book largely set the tone for subsequent work in animal ecology. The principles of the subject are admirably presented.

DOWDESWELL, W. H. *Animal Ecology*. Methuen, 1952. A good general book with several methods of study clearly explained.

KEVAN, D. K. McE. (Editor). *Soil Zoology*. Butterworth, 1955. This collection of articles includes several which bear on soil analysis, collection and counting of small animals such as springtails, identification of soil fauna, etc. The article entitled 'Ecology of the Fauna of Forest Soils', by P. W. Murphy contains much relevant material. *110383*

EDNEY, E. D. *The Water Relations of Terrestrial Arthropods.* C.U.P., 1957. An advanced book on the ways in which arthropods overcome the problems of conserving water on land.

FRIEDLANDER, C. P. and PRIEST, D. A. *Insects and Spiders.* Pitman, 1955. Keys for identifying insects down to families and many spiders down to genera. There are also ecological notes.

HINCKS, W. D. *Handbooks for the Identification of British Insects. Dermaptera and Orthoptera.* Royal Entomological Society of London, 1956. An authoritative work, but must be used carefully.

HUBBARD, C. E. *Grasses. A guide to their structure, identification, uses and distribution in the British Isles.* Penguin, 1954. Not too difficult; very informative.

STEP, E. *Bees, Wasps, Ants and Allied Orders of the British Isles.* Warne. Although an elementary book it gives a wealth of information, much of it relevant to heathland.

GENERAL INDEX

INDEX OF GENERA